EXERCISES IN PHYSICAL GEOGRAPHY

BY THE SAME AUTHOR

The Earth Sciences, Harper and Row, 1963
Introduction to Physical Geography, Wiley, 1965
Physical Geography, 3rd Edition, Wiley, 1969

EXERCISES IN PHYSICAL GEOGRAPHY

ARTHUR N. STRAHLER

Columbia University

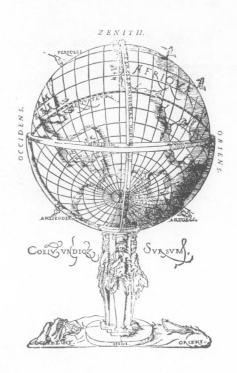

JOHN WILEY & SONS, INC.   New York · London · Sydney · Toronto

Sixteenth century globe on title page. (Courtesy of Cosmographia Petri Apiani, 1551.)

CONTENTS

INTRODUCTION

The exercises in this manual serve two basic purposes. One is to help you to develop technical skills in handling the data of physical geography; the other is to develop your ability to interpret the data of physical geography.

Cartographic skills are a prime essential for the geographer, because practically all of his information on spatial distributions of variables over the earth's surface is stored and displayed on maps. Map reading requires attention to details, as well as constant awareness of scales, distances, and directions. Map making requires precision and accuracy.

Many kinds of physical properties are represented by line of equal value (isopleths) drawn on a flat map. Such lines add a third dimension of information and depict a continuous surface that reveals distributional patterns and rates of change. You should come to feel as much at home in constructing isobars and isotherms, as in drawing topographic contours.

Quantitative geography makes use of the graphical representation of two variable quantities on a rectangular coordinate field. Accurate plotting of numerical data is required in almost every area of physical geography. The skills you gain in preparation of the many graphs in this manual are easily transferred to other branches of geography. It is important to know how the logarithmic (constant-ratio) scale is constituted and when its use is required.

Wherever possible, you are asked to interpret the data you have plotted on graphs or drawn on maps. Explanation is, after all, the final goal of any scientific investigation. Questions that cannot be answered with finality at least call for invention of one or more reasonable hypothesis.

HOW TO USE THE EXERCISE MANUAL

The pages of this exercise manual are perforated for easy removal. Pages headed by blank spaces for name, date, and course designation are intended to be removed for completion and later turned in to your instructor for checking. Perform the required graphic operations and answer the questions directly on these pages. Among the basic tools you will need throughout the program are a straightedge, pencil, compass, protractor, and dividers.

TEXTBOOK REFERENCES

The exercises are designed primarily for use with *Physical Geography, 3rd. Edition,* by Arthur N. Strahler, 1969, John Wiley and Sons, New York. In addition, most of the exercises apply equally well to *Introduction to Physical Geography,* 1965, by the same author and publisher.

The twenty-nine exercise groups, alphabetically designated, correspond closely with chapters in the reference texts. The relevant chapter numbers and pages are given on the opening page of each exercise group. You will find that the subjects covered by the exercises are fully explained and illustrated in the parent textbook.

Group A

EARTH FORM; THE GEOGRAPHIC GRID

Text References

Strahler, 1969, *Physical Geography, 3rd Edition*, Chapter 1, pp. 5—18.
Strahler, 1970, *Introduction to Physical Geography, 2nd Edition*, Chapter 1, pp. 3—8.

Formulas for use in Exercises A-1 through A-4:

K = Distance, in miles
d = Divergence, in feet

Approximate: $K = 1\,1/3\,\sqrt{h}$

Exact: $K = 1.317\,\sqrt{h}$

Approximate: $h = 3/5\,K^2$

Exact: $h = 0.574\,K^2$

Formula for use with Exercise A-5:

$$\text{Oblateness} = \frac{a - b}{a}$$

where a = equatorial diameter = 9726.68 mi.

and b = polar diameter = 7899.98 mi.

Exercise A-1

What is the most distant point on the sea surface visible from an eye point at each of the following heights? (Show formula used and calculations. Answers in miles.)

        (a) Eye point 49 feet above sea level. Ans. _____mi

        (b) Eye point 121 feet above sea level. Ans. _____mi

        (c) Eye point 4900 ft above sea level. Ans. _____mi

Exercise A-2

A shore battery is firing shells into a floating target 25 ft high and 20 mi distant.

        (a) Is any part of the target visible to an observer at the battery whose eye point is 50 ft above sea level? (Show formula and calculations.)

                                        Ans. _____

(Continue on reverse side of page)

(b) Would any part of the target be visible to an observer whose eye level is 400 ft above sea level?

Ans. _____

Exercise A-3

At a distance of 12 mi the tips of a ship's funnels are just on the horizon as seen through a submarine periscope at sea level. How high above sea level do the ship's funnels rise? (Show formula and calculations. Answer in feet.)

Ans. _____

Exercise A-4

Survivors on a life raft are 17 mi from a lighthouse. The light source is 100 ft above sea level. The maximum eye level of the survivors is 6 ft above the sea surface.

(a) Can the survivors see the rays from the lighthouse? (Show formula and calculations.)

Ans. _____

(b) Calculate the distance at which light rays would just barely be visible on the horizon.

Ans. _____

Exercise A-5

(a) Using the formula on page 3, determine exactly the earth's oblateness. (Show formula, and calculations. Carry answer to four significant figures.)

Ans. _____

(b) On a perfectly scaled globe, 10 in. in equatorial diameter, how much shorter would the polar diameter be than the equatorial diameter? (Show calculations.)

Ans. _____

Exercise A-6

Using a small globe and a piece of thin string or a rubber band, make great circle courses between each of the cities listed below. For each route, list the principal cities or geographical features lying on or very near the route.

(a) Seattle – Tokyo _____

_____

_____

(b) New York – Liverpool _____

_____

_____

(c) New York – Bombay _____

_____

_____

_____

(d) Colombo – Buenos Aires _____

_____

_____

(e) Miami – Capetown _____

_____

_____

(Continue on reverse side of page)

Exercise A-7

Using a small globe, give as closely as possible the latitude and longitude of the following cities:

New York, N.Y.   lat. _____ long. _____

Capetown, S. Africa   lat. _____ long. _____

Shanghai, China   lat. _____ long. _____

Honolulu, Hawaii   lat. _____ long. _____

London, England   lat. _____ long. _____

Rio de Janeiro, Brazil   lat. _____ long. _____

Exercise A-8

What error has been made in each of the following notations? Encircle the error and explain below.

(a) Lat. 5° 08′ 31″ S, long. 191° 33′ 04″ W

_____

_____

(b) Lat. 89° 71′ 23″ N, long. 88° 21′ 56″ E

_____

_____

(c) Lat. 21° 43′ 59″ E, long. 177° 03′ 00″ E

_____

_____

(d) Lat. 94° 21′ 10″ N, long. 103° 42′ 51″ W

_____

_____

(e) Lat. 48° 57′ 45″ N, long. 02° 00′ 31″ N

_____

_____

Exercise A-9

Show, by a geometric construction, that a degree of longitude at the 60th parallel is one-half as long as a degree of longitude at the equator. In the diagram below, draw lines and angles required in your proof. In the space below the diagram give a complete step-by-step statement of the proof.

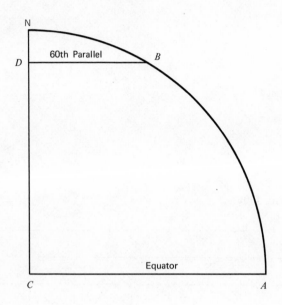

Exercise A-10

From how many different starting points on the globe would it be possible to travel 100 mi north, then 100 mi east (or west), then 100 mi south, and be exactly at the starting point? (The southern-hemisphere case is simple, but can you solve this problem fully for the northern hemisphere?)

Use these diagrams for schematic drawings of your proposed solutions:

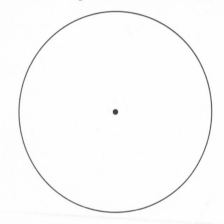

Southern Hemisphere

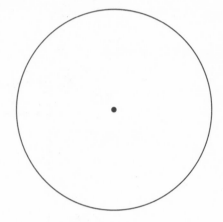

Northern Hemisphere

Use the space below to explain fully:

_____
_____
_____
_____
_____
_____
_____
_____
_____
_____
_____
_____
_____
_____

Optional project

Derive a mathematical equation that will express fully and precisely the complete solution of the problem for the northern hemisphere.

10

Group B
MAP PROJECTIONS

B

Text References

Strahler, 1969, *Physical Geography, 3rd Edition,* Chapter 2, pp. 19-42.
Strahler, 1970, *Introduction to Physical Geography, 2nd Edition,* Chapter 1, pp. 8-21.

List of Map Projections for Exercises B-1 and B-2

Code		Name of Projection
1		Orthographic
	1-P	Polar
	1-E	Equatorial
	1-O	Oblique (Tilted)
2		Stereographic
	2-P	Polar
	2-E	Equatorial
	2-O	Oblique (Tilted)
3		Gnomonic
	3-P	Polar
	3-E	Equatorial
	3-O	Oblique (Tilted)
4		Azimuthal Equidistant
	4-P	Polar
	4-E	Equatorial
	4-O	Oblique (Tilted)
5		Azimuthal Equal-area
	5-P	Polar
	5-E	Equatorial
	5-O	Oblique (Tilted)
6		Perspective Conic
7		Lambert Conformal Conic
8		Polyconic
9		Equatorial Mercator
10		Transverse Mercator
11		Mollweide Homolographic
12		Sinusoidal
13		Homolosine (Goode's)
14		Eckert IV

Exercise B-1 PROPERTIES OF MAP PROJECTIONS

Refer to the list of projections on page 11. Listed below are 14 statements relating to projections on the list. Select those projections for which the statement is true. Enter the code numbers of the projections in the blank spaces below each statement. Write the code numbers in the same sequence as on the list. Consider polar, equatorial, and oblique (tilted) positions as separate projections.

(a)   All are equal-area projections.

____   ____   ____   ____   ____   ____   ____   ____   ____   ____

____   ____   ____   ____   ____   ____   ____   ____   ____   ____

(b)   All are conformal projections.

____   ____   ____   ____   ____   ____   ____   ____   ____   ____

____   ____   ____   ____   ____   ____   ____   ____   ____   ____

(c)   All are neither equal-area nor conformal.

____   ____   ____   ____   ____   ____   ____   ____   ____   ____

____   ____   ____   ____   ____   ____   ____   ____   ____   ____

(d)   All the parallels are curved lines.

____   ____   ____   ____   ____   ____   ____   ____   ____   ____

____   ____   ____   ____   ____   ____   ____   ____   ____   ____

(e)   All the parallels are straight lines.

____   ____   ____   ____   ____   ____   ____   ____   ____   ____

____   ____   ____   ____   ____   ____   ____   ____   ____   ____

(f)   All the meridians, except the central meridians, are curved lines.

____   ____   ____   ____   ____   ____   ____   ____   ____   ____

____   ____   ____   ____   ____   ____   ____   ____   ____   ____

(g)   All the meridians are straight lines.

____   ____   ____   ____   ____   ____   ____   ____   ____   ____

____   ____   ____   ____   ____   ____   ____   ____   ____   ____

(Continue on reverse side of page.)

(h)   All the curved parallels and meridians are true arcs of circles.

———   ———   ———   ———   ———   ———   ———   ———   ———   ———

———   ———   ———   ———   ———   ———   ———   ———   ———   ———

(i)   All the parallels are arcs of circles, but not necessarily concentric.

———   ———   ———   ———   ———   ———   ———   ———   ———   ———

———   ———   ———   ———   ———   ———   ———   ———   ———   ———

(j)   All the parallels and meridians intersect at true right angles.

———   ———   ———   ———   ———   ———   ———   ———   ———   ———

———   ———   ———   ———   ———   ———   ———   ———   ———   ———

(k)   Neither pole can be shown.

———   ———   ———   ———   ———   ———   ———   ———   ———   ———

———   ———   ———   ———   ———   ———   ———   ———   ———   ———

(l)   Only one pole can be shown at a time.

———   ———   ———   ———   ———   ———   ———   ———   ———   ———

———   ———   ———   ———   ———   ———   ———   ———   ———   ———

(m)   Map outline is circular when exactly one hemisphere is shown.

———   ———   ———   ———   ———   ———   ———   ———   ———   ———

———   ———   ———   ———   ———   ———   ———   ———   ———   ———

(n)   The projection can be constructed by drawing lines or rays from a single point, through a globe, onto a flat surface or a developable surface.

———   ———   ———   ———   ———   ———   ———   ———   ———   ———

———   ———   ———   ———   ———   ———   ———   ———   ———   ———

Exercise B-2 MAP PROJECTION SUMMARY CHART

A blank chart is provided in four parts on the following pages. Trim and join the four sheets to form a single chart. In each blank space enter the appropriate information about the map projection. Information in the final two columns (Inventor, Year; Historical notes) will require library research and may be regarded as an optional special project.

Exercise B-3 CONSTRUCTION OF MAP PROJECTIONS

Five of the simpler map projections are to be constructed, using only a pencil, straightedge, protractor, and compass. A basic construction diagram is provided for each projection. Refer to textbook illustrations for construction details. Use a sharp pencil point and plot angles with extreme care.

A complete set of meridians and parallels should be plotted and labeled for every 15° of arc (e.g., 0°, 15°, 30°, 45°, 60°, 75°, 90°, etc.).

As an optional special project, transcribe the outlines of the continents on each projection. Refer to an atlas or globe for information.

The following detailed instructions apply to individual projections:

(a)   Orthographic, polar position. Plot northern hemisphere.

(b)   Stereographic, polar position. Limit the map to the northern hemisphere. If desired, portions of parallels 15°S and 30°S can be added.

(c)   Azimuthal equidistant, polar position. Center map on north pole. Plot entire globe. Label south pole.

(d)   Azimuthal equal-area, polar position. Center map on north pole. Plot entire globe. Label south pole.

(e)   Perspective conic, one standard parallel. Cone is tangent on 45th parallel. Show northern hemisphere only. Label standard parallel. Note that 360° of longitude will comprise less than a full circle.

(f)   *Optional project.* Sinusoidal projection. Construct meridians to complete the eastern hemisphere, following detailed instructions on page.

Exercise B-2 MAP PROJECTION SUMMARY CHART

Name of Projection	Class	Complete Outline, Maximum Coverage	Positions	Form of Meridians: Straight? Curved? Curve Form?	Form of Parallels: Straight? Curved? Curve Form?
1 ORTHOGRAPHIC			Polar		
			Equatorial		
			Oblique		
2 STEREOGRAPHIC			P		
			E		
			O		
3 GNOMONIC			P		
			E		
			O		
4 AZIMUTHAL EQUIDISTANT			P		
			E		
			O		
5 AZIMUTHAL EQUAL-AREA			P		
			E		
			O		

Join to line C-D on page 21

B₂

E

Name _____ Date _____ Course No. _____ Section _____

Conformal? Equal-Area? Neither?	Unique Properties	Best Uses	Inventor, Year	Historical Notes

D

Join to line D-E on page 23

A

Trim and join to line A-B on page 17

B

19

C — Trim and join to line C-D on page 17 — D

6	PERSPECTIVE CONIC					
7	LAMBERT CONFORMAL CONIC					
8	POLYCONIC					
9	EQUATORIAL MERCATOR					
10	TRANSVERSE MERCATOR					
11	MOLLWEIDE HOMOLOGRAPHIC					
12	SINUSOIDAL					
13	HOMOLOSINE (GOODE'S)					
14	ECKERT IV					

Trim and join to line D-F on page 23

F

B_2

B₂

E

Trim and join to line D-E on page 19

D

Trim and join to line D-F on page 21

F

Draw projection here

Construction diagram

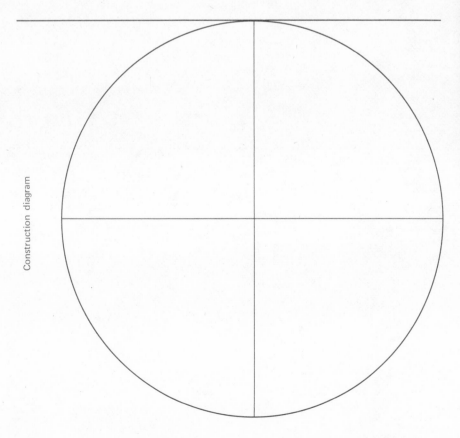

Exercise B-3 (a) ORTHOGRAPHIC PROJECTION, POLAR POSITION

B₃

Draw projection here

Construction
diagram

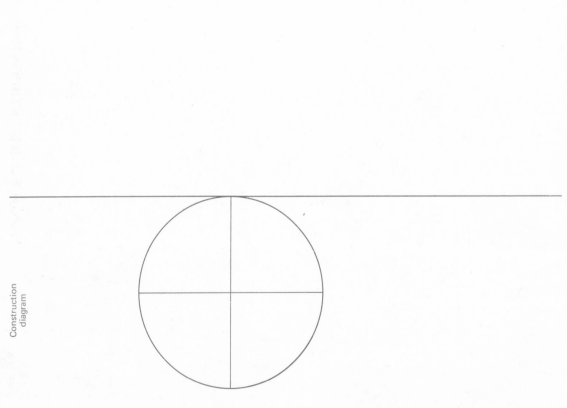

Exercise B-3 (b) STEREOGRAPHIC PROJECTION, POLAR POSITION

26

Name_____Date_____
Course No._____Section_____

B₃

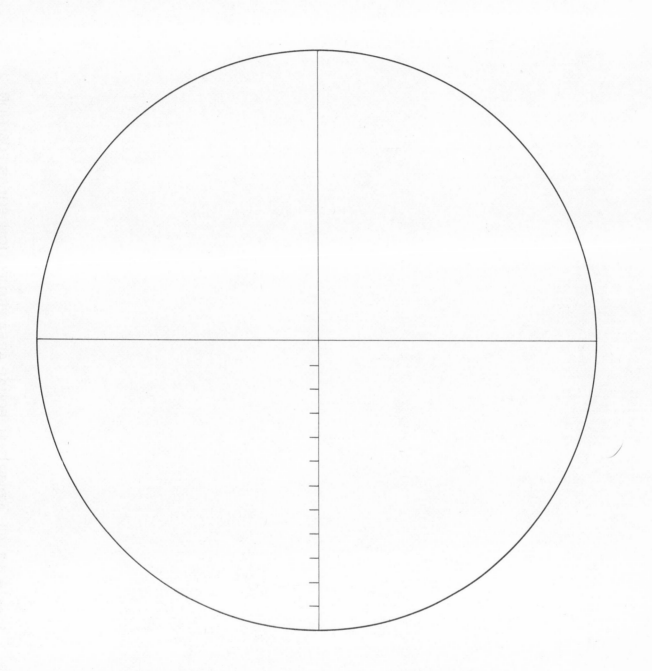

Exercise B-3 (c) AZIMUTHAL EQUIDISTANT PROJECTION, POLAR POSITION

B₃

Draw projection here

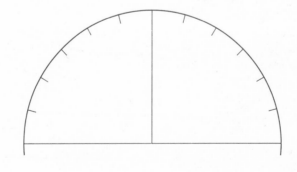

Construction
diagram

Exercise B-3 (d) AZIMUTHAL EQUAL AREA PROJECTION, POLAR POSITION

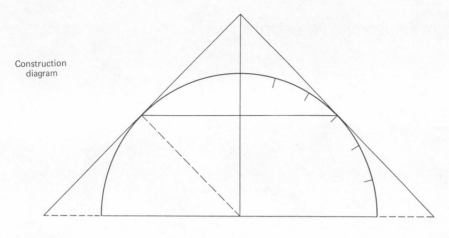

Construction
diagram

Draw projection
below

+

**Exercise B-3 (e) PERSPECTIVE CONIC PROJECTION, ONE STANDARD
PARALLEL, 45°N**

B₃

Exercise B-3 (f) SINUSOIDAL PROJECTION

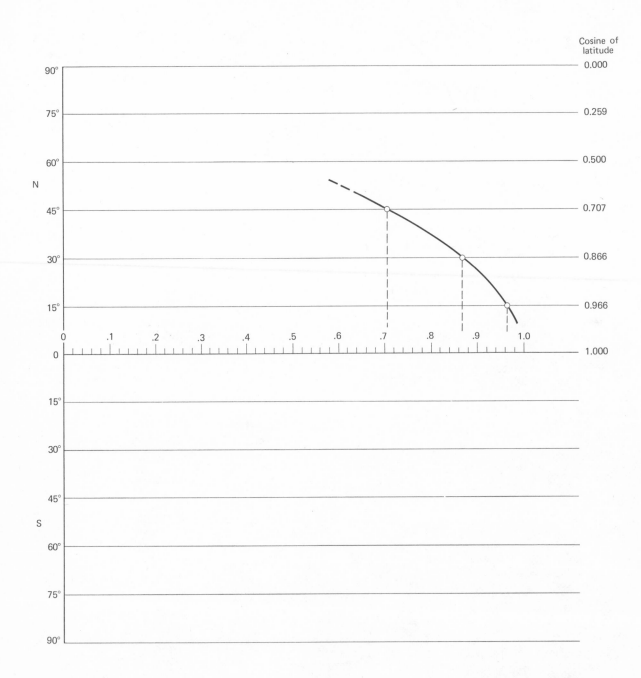

Distance from prime meridian to a given meridian varies as cosine of latitude (given on scale at right). First plot the 180th meridian, using the scale printed on the equator, as indicated by the partially drawn meridian. Draw meridians for 60° and 120°. This may be done by dividing the cosine values into thirds, or by using an engineer's scale. For the 180th meridian the 20th scale applies; for 120th meridian use 30th scale; for 60th meridian use 60th scale. If desired, additional meridians may be drawn for 30° intervals.

LOCATION AND DIRECTION ON THE GLOBE

C

Text references

Strahler, 1969, *Physical Geography,* 3rd Edition, Chapter 3, pp. 43–63.
Strahler, 1970, *Introduction to Physical Geography, 2nd Edition,* Appendix II, pp. 431–435.

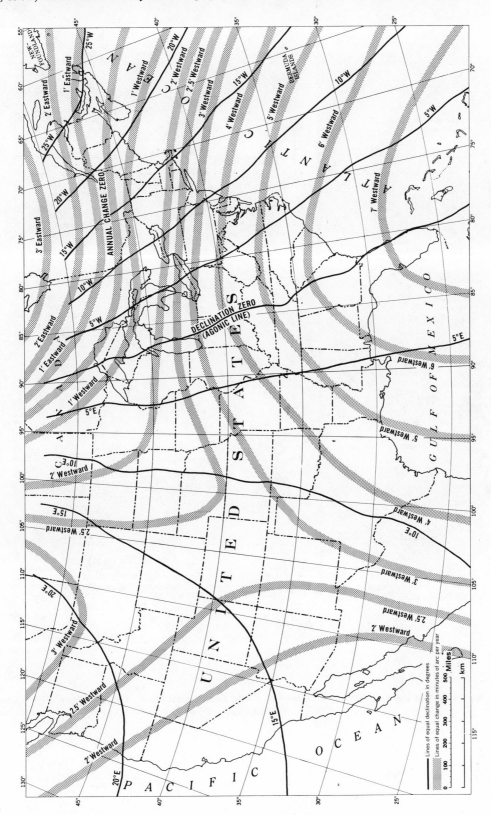

Map to accompany Exercise C-1. Isogonic map of United States for 1965. (U.S. Coast & Geodetic Survey)

C

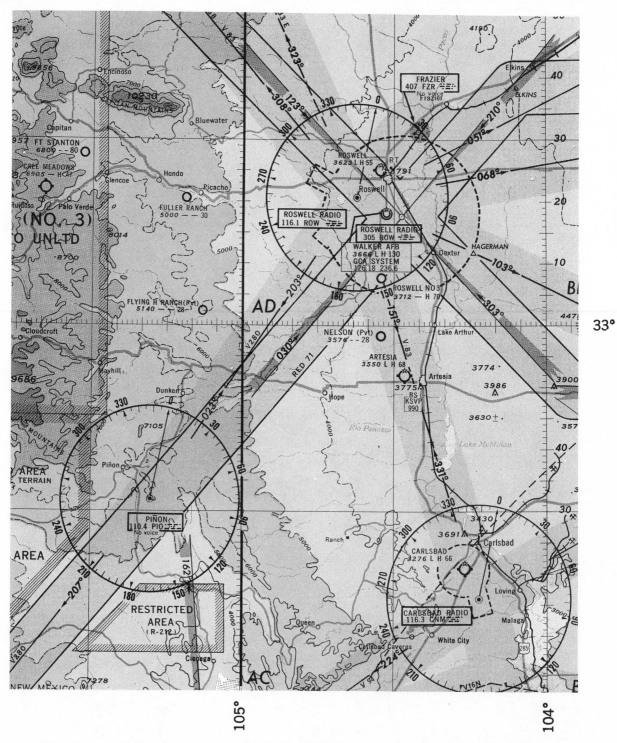

Map to accompany Exercise C-2. Portion of Sheet 406, World Aeronautical Chart. (Reduced from original scale of 1:1,000,000.)

Name_____Date_____

Course No._____Section_____

Exercise C-1 MAGNETIC DECLINATION

Refer to the isogonic map of the United States on page 31.

(a) Estimate the magnetic declination at the following places in 1965. (Give answer to nearest one-half degree.)

Miami, Florida _____

Boston, Massachusetts _____

San Franscisco, California _____

New Orleans, Louisiana _____

Chicago, Illinois _____

Vancouver, British Columbia _____

Halifax, Nova Scotia _____

(b) Estimate the annual change in declination at the following places. (Give answer to nearest one-half minute.)

Denver, Colorado _____

Toronto, Ontario _____

Tucson, Arizona _____

Atlanta, Georgia _____

(c) The isogonic map is drawn for the year 1965. Estimate the required correction in magnetic declination at each of the following places, for the stated year. (Show calculations.)

Salt Lake City, Utah, 1970   Ans._____

Baltimore, Maryland, 1974   Ans._____

Halifax, Nova Scotia, 1977   Ans._____

Cincinnati, Ohio, 1950   Ans._____

C₂

Exercise C-2 GEOGRAPHIC COORDINATES AND MAGNETIC BEARINGS

Refer to the air-navigation chart on page 32.

(a) Give the geographic coordinates, to the nearest minute, for each of the following places:

Artesia (town) lat. _____ long. _____

Roswell Radio lat. _____ long. _____

Carlsbad Airport lat. _____ long. _____

Hondo lat. _____ long. _____

(b) Using a protractor, estimate the magnetic declination in this area.

Ans. _____

For comparison, determine declination from the isogonic map.

Ans. _____

(c) What is the magnetic bearing of a line from Carlsbad Airport to Pinon Radio?

Ans. _____

(d) What is the magnetic bearing of a line from Fuller Ranch Airport to Roswell Radio?

Ans. _____

(e) What is the true bearing of a line from Hope to Picacho?

Ans. _____

(f) What is the true bearing of a line from Cienaga to Lake Arthur?

Ans. _____

(g) Determine the following distances in nautical miles. (Read to nearest one-half nautical mile.)

Hope to Picacho _____

Cienaga to Lake Arthur _____

(h) On the line below, construct a graphic scale in statute miles for the air-navigation map. Show 10-mile subdivisions and a total length of 100 miles. On the lower line, construct a graphic scale in kilometers.

0

Miles

0

Kilometers

Exercise C-3 MILITARY GRID COORDINATES AND AZIMUTHS

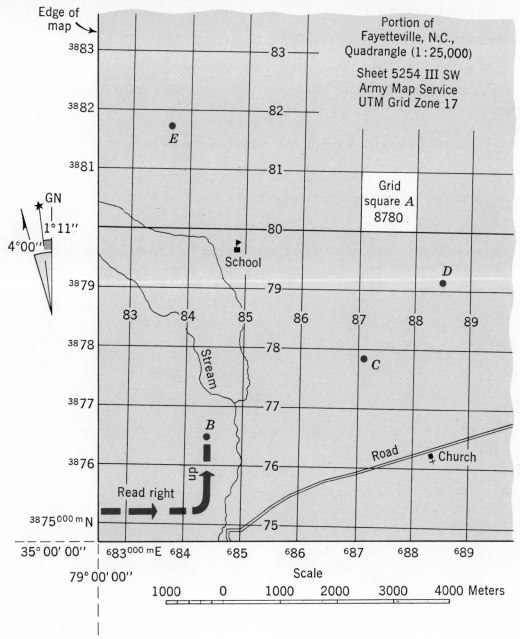

QUESTIONS

(a) Give the grid designation of the square in which the letter *D* is printed.

_____ meters east   Grid designation

_____ meters north   _____

(b) Give grid coordinates to the nearest 100 m of the point *E*.

_____ meters east   Grid coordinates

_____ meters north   _____

(continue on reverse side of page)

35

C₃

(c) Find the following points on the map. Mark each point precisely with an "X." Label with corresponding letter.

        Point F 865758

        Point G 834787

(d) Using a protractor, measure the grid declination.

                         Ans. _____

(e) Determine the grid azimuth of a line from Point C to the center point of grid square A.

                         Ans. _____

(f) Determine the grid azimuth of a line from Point B to a point (unmarked) at 833794.

                         Ans. _____

(g) Determine magnetic azimuth (magnetic bearing) of a line from Point F to Point G.

                         Ans. _____

(h) Connect points D, E, G, and F with straight lines. Determine the total distance required to complete this quadrilateral traverse.

Distance D to E	_____	km
E to G	_____	km
G to F	_____	km
F to D	_____	km
Total	_____	km

Name_____ Date_____

Course No._____ Section_____

C4

Exercise C-4 U. S. LAND OFFICE GRID SYSTEM

Printed below is a portion of the Redfield, South Dakota, Quadrangle showing sections of land and a standard parallel (U. S. Geological Survey).

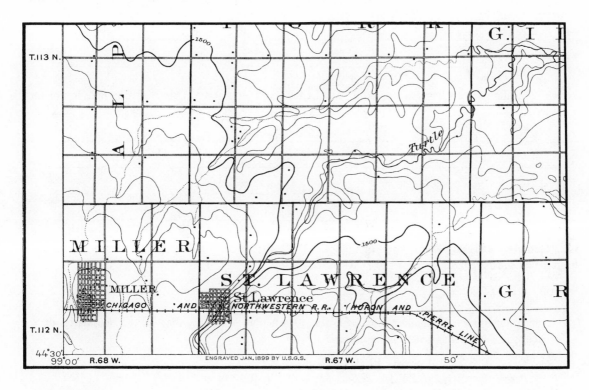

QUESTIONS

(a) On the map above, number all sections with their correct numbers according to the established system shown in the accompanying diagram (below, left).

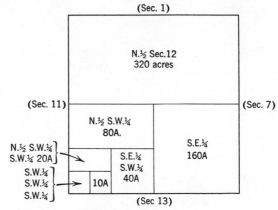

Sections within a township

Subdivisions of a section

(Continue on reverse side of page)

C₄

(b) Find the *standard parallel* on the map. Why are north-south section and township boundaries offset along this parallel? Explain fully.

_____

_____

_____

_____

_____

_____

(c) Explain why the sections beneath the word "MILLER" (bold letters) are more than one mile in north-south extent.

_____

_____

_____

_____

(d) State accurately and fully the location of the letter "T" in the word "Turtle" on the map. (Refer to diagrams on previous page.)

Ans. _____

(e) Locate on the map each of the parcels of land described below. Carefully draw in the boundaries of each parcel and label with corresponding letter.

>   *Parcel A*   NE 1/4 of Sec. 19, T.113 N, R.67 W
>   *Parcel B*   N 1/2 of SW 1/4 of Sec. 35, T.113 N, R.67 W
>   *Parcel C*   SW 1/4 of NE 1/4 of Sec. 13, T.112 N, R.68 W

Special Project (A). Consult the *General Land Office Map of the United States* (U. S. Department of the Interior, 1937) and determine which principal meridian is used for ranges within the exercise map area.

Ans. _____

Special Project (B). Determine the number of *chains* (surveyor's measure of length) in a mile. On the diagram of section subdivisions (reverse side of this page) label the lengths, in chains, of the sides of each land parcel shown. Insert the numbers of square chains contained in each parcel.

Group D

ILLUMINATION OF THE GLOBE

D

Text References

Strahler, 1969, *Physical Geography, 3rd Edition,* Chapter 4, pp. 65–82.
Strahler, 1970, *Introduction to Physical Geography, 2nd Edition,* Chapter 2, pp. 23–32.

Exercise D-1 CONSTRUCTION OF ELLIPSES

Construct ellipses of different sizes and degrees of ellipticity; use the space provided on page 41. Remove
the page and place it on a drawing board, or other soft surface. Fasten the page to the board with pieces of
tape. Tie a fine thread into a loop which is 4 inches long, doubled length. This operation is facilitated by
tying the thread in a loop around two drawing pins that have been placed 4 inches apart. Use a square knot.
(The loop length need not be exactly 4 in., but not longer or shorter by more than 1/8 in.) Insert drawing
pins (push-pins, thumbtacks, or needles are satisfactory) firmly into the board at points marked F_1 along the
line of the major axis, one on either side of the center point C. Slip the thread loop over the pins. Insert a well-sharpened pencil point in the loop and pull taut. Allow the loop to guide the pencil point in a
full circuit, drawing an ellipse.
Similarly, draw ellipses with foci at F_2 and F_3. Observe the effect of wider separation of foci upon the
form of the ellipse.
Using the innermost ellipse, label the following: *focus* (2), *radius vector* (2), *ellipse, major axis, minor axis.*
Using a pencil compass, fit a true circle to the outermost ellipse. Attempt to place the circle in such a way
that its area is exactly equal to the area of the ellipse.

Exercise D-2 THE EARTH'S ELLIPTICAL ORBIT

In the space provided on page 43, construct an ellipse to represent the earth's orbit. Use the same 4-in.
thread loop as in Exercise D-1. Place the drawing pins at foci marked F_1 and F_2.
You will notice that the major axis of the ellipse is obliquely inclined to the center line of the page. Dashed
lines, at right angles to each other, intersect at F_2 to represent the sun at one focus of the ellipse. Those
points at which the dashed lines intersect the ellipse you have drawn represent solstices and equinoxes.
Place arrows on the orbit to represent direction of revolution. Locate *perihelion* and *aphelion.* Give dates.
Label distances from earth to sun at perihelion and aphelion.
Locate and label Vernal equinox, Summer solstice, Autumnal equinox, and Winter solstice. Give dates.
Label the four quadrants of the ellipse with names of the four astronomical seasons: Spring, Summer,
Autumn, and Winter.
Answer questions on page 44 to complete this exercise.

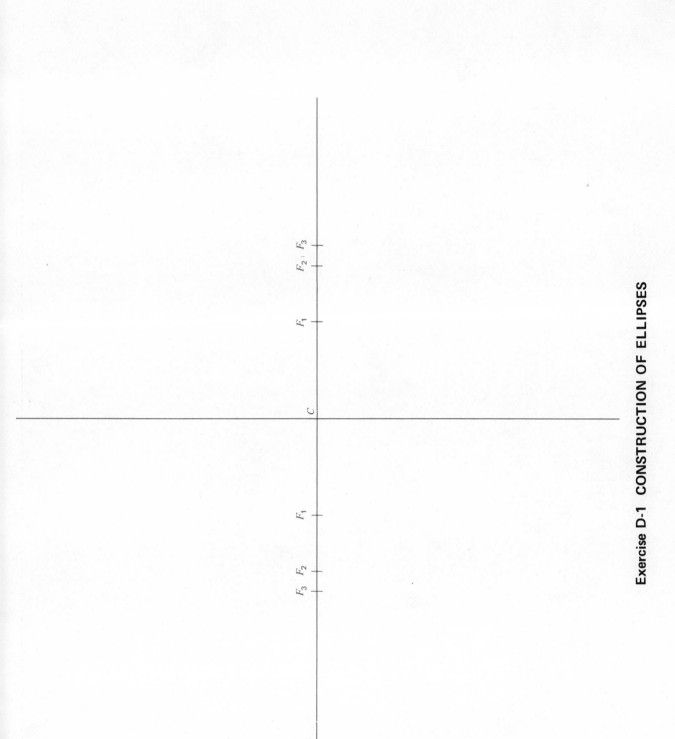

Exercise D-1 CONSTRUCTION OF ELLIPSES

F_1

C

F_2

Major
axis

Exercise D-2 THE EARTH'S ELLIPTICAL ORBIT

D₂

(a) How many days elapse between winter solstice and perihelion?

Ans. _____

Between summer solstice and aphelion?

Ans. _____

(b) List the astronomical seasons in order of the length of time each season endures. Give shortest season first; longest last.

Shortest _____

_____

_____

Longest _____

Explain below the method by which you determined the above sequence of lengths of seasons.

_____

_____

_____

_____

_____

_____

_____

_____

Optional special project

Consult an almanac for the exact times of solstices and equinoxes for an entire astronomical year. Determine the elapsed time from each equinox to the next solstice, and from solstice to the next equinox. Total the four periods. Does the total agree with the exact value of the tropical year? Give complete data in the space below. Label the lengths of seasons on the diagram.

Exercise D-3 EQUINOXES AND SOLSTICES

The diagram below represents a view of the earth from a point above the plane of the orbit (plane of the ecliptic). Label each equinox and solstice and give date. Add arrows to show direction of earth rotation and revolution. The dashed line halving each globe represents the circle of illumination. Shade the dark half of each globe. Mark the points of noon, midnight, sunrise, and sunset with the letters *N*, *M*, *R*, and *S*, respectively.

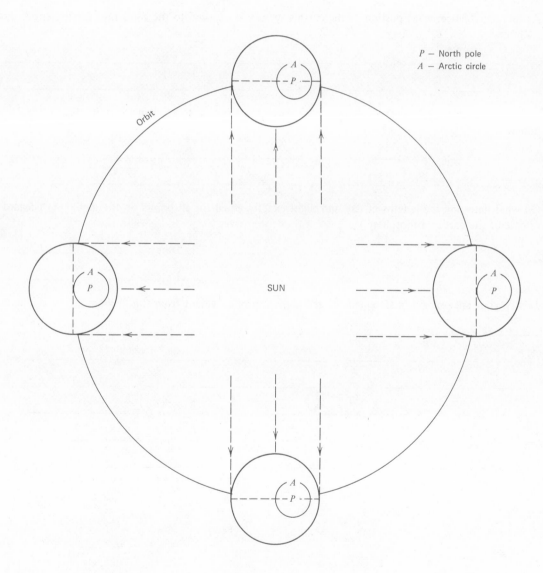

P — North pole
A — Arctic circle

(Answer questions on reverse of page.)

D3

QUESTIONS

(a) On what dates does the circle of illumination pass through the north pole? (Give name of solstice or equinox, and date)

_____ Date _____

_____ Date _____

(b) On what dates is the circle of illumination exactly tangent to the Artic Circle?

_____ Date _____

_____ Date _____

(c) At summer solstice, what portion of the earth's surface is exposed to the sun's rays for the entire day of 24 hours?

_____

_____

(d) At winter solstice, what portion of the earth's surface is exposed to the sun's rays for the entire 24 hours?

_____

_____

(e) On what dates are the lengths of day and night exactly equal for all points on the globe? (Disregard effects of the earth's atmosphere.)

_____ Date _____

_____ Date _____

Justify your answer with a statement of geometrical proof, evident from the diagram.

_____

_____

_____

_____

_____

_____

Exercise D-4 SUN'S PATH IN THE SKY

Give the *parallel of latitude* (degrees N or S) or *pole* (N or S) for which each of the following statements is true. (Assume that the earth is perfectly spherical and has no atmosphere.)

(a) Day and night are always of equal length (three answers).

_____   _____   _____

(b) The sun's noon altitude is 90° on June 21.

_____

(c) The sun's noon altitude is 50° on September 23 (two answers).

_____   _____

(d) The sun at midnight on December 22 is exactly on the horizon at a point due south.

_____

(e) The path of the sun in the sky at all times of year lies in a plane perpendicular to the horizon plane.

_____

(f) The sun at noon on December 22 is exactly on the horizon at a point due south.

_____

(g) The path of the sun in the sky at all times of the year lies in a plane inclined 45° with the plane of the horizon (two answers).

_____   _____

(h) On March 21 the sun's noon altitude is 66½° (two answers).

_____   _____

(i) Throughout the day the shadow of a vertical rod sweeps clockwise around the rod at the rate of 15 per hour and remains the same length.

_____

(j) The shadow of a straight east-west wall with a straight, horizontal top remains the same width from midmorning to midafternoon and is as wide as the wall is high.

_____

(k) The shadow of a vertical rod points due west during the morning, then due east during the afternoon.

_____

(l) The circle of illumination bisects the parallel on August 9.

_____

D5

Exercise D-5 LATITUDE AND SUN'S ALTITUDE

Given the following information, find the latitude of the place:

Noon Sun Altitude	Latitude at Which Sun's Rays Strike Earth Perpendicularly at Noon	Date	Latitude of Place
(a) 11°	Not given	Sept. 23	_____
(b) 44½°	12°N	Not given	_____
(c) 90°	Not given	March 21	_____
(d) 90°	Not given	June 21	_____
(e) 0°	20°S	Not given	_____
(f) 8½°	Not given	Dec. 22	_____
(g) 81°	9°S	Not given	_____

Exercise D-6 SUN'S PATH WITH VARIOUS AXIAL INCLINATIONS

Instead of the existing situation, in which the earth's axis is inclined at an angle of 66½° with plane of the ecliptic, we imagine various other angles of inclination: 45°, 10°, 0°, and 90°. (*Note:* The planet Uranus has an axial inclination 8° from the plane of the ecliptic.)

Sketch the sun's path at equinox and both solstices for the axial inclination and latitude specified in each case. Label paths.

On each diagram label the following: horizon, cardinal points (N, E, S, W), nadir, zenith, celestial meridian. Locate and label *Polaris.*

(a) Inclination 45°, latitude 90°N (north pole).

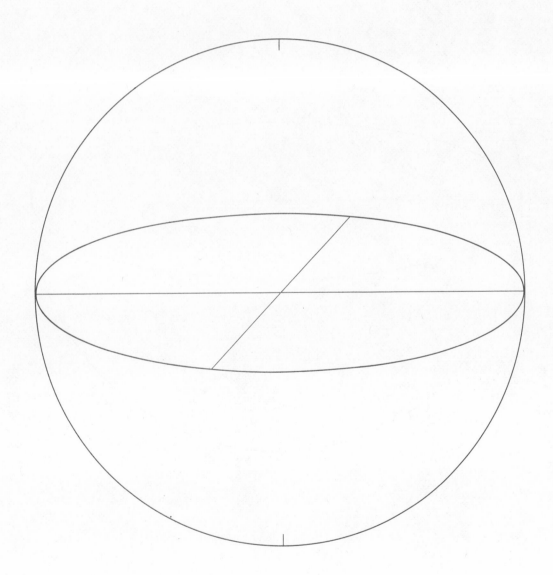

(b) Inclination 10°, latitude 40°N.

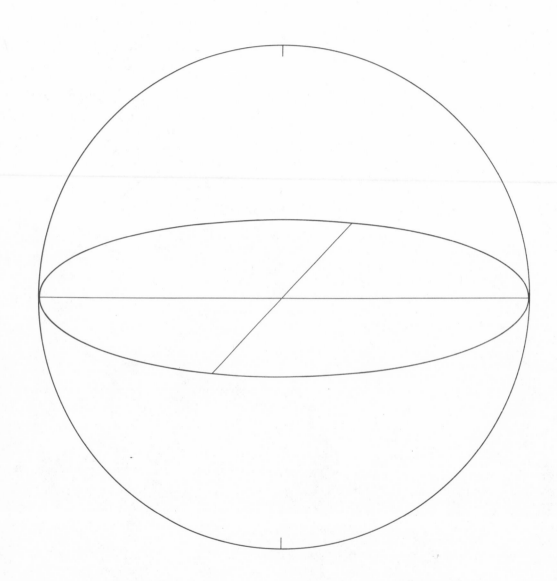

Exercise D-6 *(Continued)*

(Refer to instructions on page 49)
(c) Inclination 0°, latitude 0° (equator).

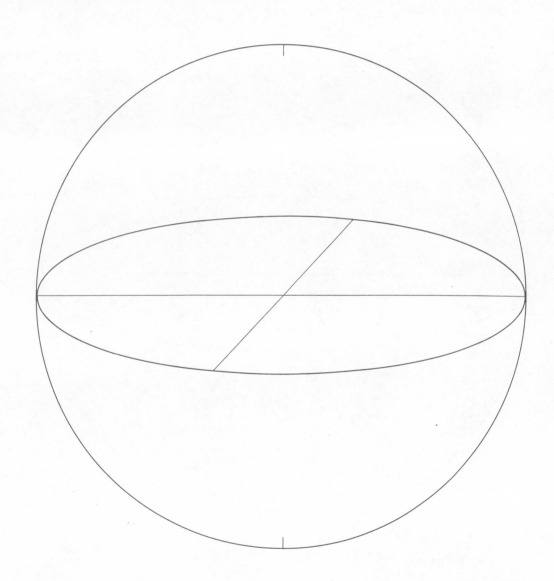

D₆

(d) Inclination 90°, latitude 66½° S (Antarctic Circle).

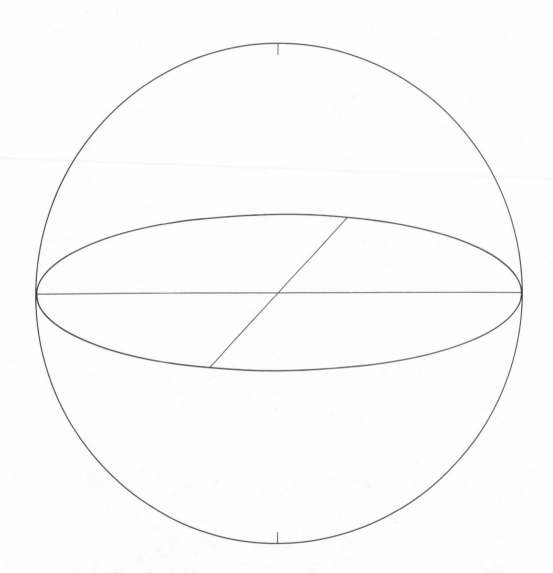

Name _____ Date _____

Course No. _____ Section _____

D7

Exercise D-7 TIMES OF SUNRISE AND SUNSET AT SOLSTICES

Use a small globe as illustrated in the diagram at right. Place a thin rubber band around the globe so as to form a great circle (illumination circle) crossing the equator at 90° E and 90° W longitude, and tangent to the arctic circle at the Greenwich meridian. The globe should have parallels of latitude at 10° intervals; meridians at 15° intervals. Use the globe as a spherical graph from which to read the times of sunrise and sunset for various parallels of latitude.

Estimate sunset and sunrise to the nearest five minutes. Enter values in the chart below. (Local time is assumed in effect.)

If no globe is available, use the stereographic hemisphere on the reverse side of this page.

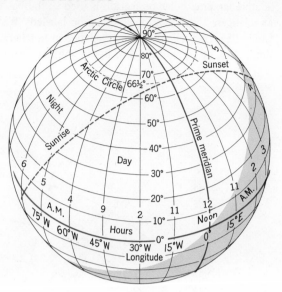

Latitude	WINTER SOLSTICE			SUMMER SOLSTICE		
	Time of Sunrise	Time of Sunset	Length of Day	Time of Sunrise	Time of Sunset	Length of Day
North 0						
10						
20						
30						
40						
50						
60						
66½						
South 10						
20						
30						
40						
50						
60						
66½						

53

STEREOGRAPHIC CHART FOR USE IN EXERCISE D-7

A stereographic polar projection is used as the basis of a graph for determining times of sunrise and sunset at solstices. The circle of illumination labeled "WS" is used for the winter solstice in northern hemisphere. Circle "SS" is used for summer solstice in northern hemisphere. The line "EQ" represents the circle of illumination at equinoxes. For use in southern hemisphere, transpose "SS" with "WS".

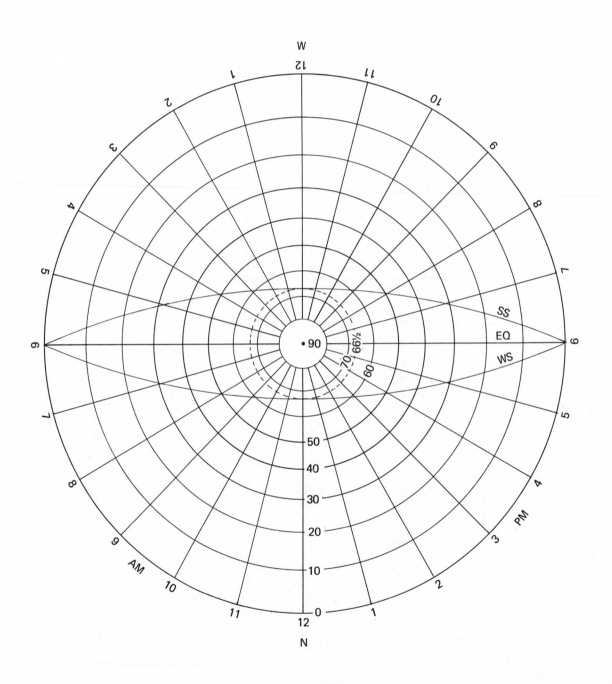

Group E

TIME

Text References

Strahler, 1969, *Physical Geography, 3rd Edition,* Chapter 5, pp. 83–96.
Strahler, 1970, *Introduction to Physical Geography, 2nd Edition,* Chapter 2, pp. 32–39.

Exercise E-1 GLOBAL STANDARD TIME

Use a small globe having 15° meridians. If no globe is available, use any political map showing national boundaries. The object of the exercise is to determine which standard time is best fitted to the position of the land area involved. First, determine which 15° meridian best represents the land area. If the area falls between two such meridians, find the intermediate meridian, which is a multiple of 7½°, and enter in the table on page 57.

Counting hours *fast* or *slow* from the Greenwich meridian, determine the standard time of each area. Enter this value in the table.

From a current world time-zone map or Almanac, determine the standard time actually in use in each area. Enter this information in the table. Note that certain countries use a time 1 hour fast of the standard meridian throughout the year. (Reference: U. S. Oceanographic Office Chart H. O. 5192.)

Exercise E-4 THE ANALEMMA

Construct an analemma by plotting the data of the table below on the graph on page 59. As shown on the graph by plotted data for January, each point is entered and marked with a small circle. A smooth curve is then drawn through the plotted points. Calendar months are marked off and labeled. Because data have been given to the nearest half-degree and half-minute, the points need not fall exactly upon a smoothly fitting curve.

Date		Equation of Time, Min.	Declination	Date		Equation of Time, Min.	Declination
Jan.	1	− 3	23° S	July	10	− 5	22½
	10	− 7	22		20	− 6½	21
	20	−11	20		30	− 6½	18½
	30	−13½	17½	Aug.	10	− 5½	16
Feb.	10	−14	15		20	− 4	12½
	20	−14	11		30	− 1	9
March	1	−13	8	Sept.	10	+ 2½	5
	10	−10½	4½		20	+ 6	1½
	20	− 8	½		30	+ 9½	2½ S
	30	− 5	3½ N	Oct.	10	+12½	6½
April	10	− 1½	7½		20	+15	10
	20	+ 1	11		30	+16	13½
	30	+ 3	14½	Nov.	10	+16	17
May	10	+ 4	17		20	+14½	19½
	20	+ 4	20		30	+11½	21½
	30	+ 3	22	Dec.	10	+ 7½	23
June	10	+ 1	23		20	+ 3	23½
	20	− 1	23½				
	30	− 3½	23				

Exercise E-1 GLOBAL STANDARD TIME (See instructions on page 55.)

Area	Best Standard Meridian	Equivalent Standard Time (Hr fast or slow)	Standard Time in Use (Hr fast or slow)
(a) Philippine Islands	_____	_____	_____
(b) Iceland	_____	_____	_____
(c) Hawaii	_____	_____	_____
(d) Spain	_____	_____	_____
(e) Guam	_____	_____	_____
(f) Ethiopia	_____	_____	_____
(g) India	_____	_____	_____
(h) Labrador	_____	_____	_____
(i) Mongolia	_____	_____	_____
(j) Guyana (Br. Guiana)	_____	_____	_____
(k) Novaya Zemlya U. S. S. R.	_____	_____	_____
(l) Northern Territory, Australia	_____	_____	_____
(m) Liberia	_____	_____	_____

(Continue on reverse side of page)

Exercise E-2 TIME AND LONGITUDE

In 1905 many nations and colonies based their time system upon a local meridian. Using the examples below, calculate the exact longitude of the meridian used. Show your calculations.

(a) Ireland. $0^h\ 25^m\ 21.1^s$ slow (meridian of Dublin).

Ans. long. ____° ____′ ____″

(b) France. $0^h\ 9^m\ 20.9^s$ fast (meridian of Paris Observatory).

Ans. long. ____° ____′ ____″

(c) Mexico. $6^h\ 36^m\ 26.7^s$ slow (meridian of the National Astronomical Observatory of Tacubaya).

Ans. long. ____° ____′ ____″

Exercise E-3 LOCAL TIME OF SUNSET

An airlines traveler, delayed at a foreign airfield, notes that the sun is setting just at the moment when his watch, set to Greenwich Civil Time when he left London, reads 1:32. The date is March 21.

(a) Assuming the sun to be on time, and disregarding effects of atmospheric refraction and sun's semidiameter, that is the observer's longitude? Show calculations (two answers).

Ans. _____

or _____

(b) On March 21, the sun is 8 minutes slow. Correct your answers to (a) so as to take this fact into account.

Ans. _____

or _____

Exercise E-4

MIN. 16 14 12 10 8 6 4 2 0 2 4 6 8 10 12 14 MIN.

Sun fast
+

Sun slow
−

24°
22°
20°
18°
16°
North 14°
12°
10°
8°
6°
4°
2°
SUN'S DECLINATION 0°
2°
4°
6°
8°
10°
South 12°
14°
16°
18° ⊙ 1/30
20° ⊙ 1/20
JANUARY
22° 1/10
⊙ 1/1
24°

MIN. 16 14 12 10 8 6 4 2 0 2 4 6 8 10 12 14 MIN.

THE ANALEMMA, SHOWING DECLINATION OF SUN AND EQUATION OF TIME

59

E₄

QUESTIONS

Using the analemma you have constructed, solve the following problems. Show computations.

(a) What will be the altitude of the noon sun at New York City (41°N lat.) on the following dates?

	Feb. 25	Aug. 25
Sun's declination	_____°	_____°
Latitude of N. Y.	41 °	41 °
Difference (algebraic)	_____°	_____°
Sun's altitude	_____°	_____°

(b) According to a clock set for Central Standard Time, at what time will the noon sun be over the meridian at Amarillo, Texas (102°W long.), on October 5?

Sun on time on standard meridian 12:00

Correction for longitude . . . . _____min

Corrected time . . . . _____

Correction for equation of time . . . . _____min

Corrected time of noon at Amarillo . . . . _____(Ans.)

(c) At what time, according to a clock set for Indian Standard Time (5½ hours fast), will the sun rise at Bombay (73°E long.) on September 23? (On the date of equinox, the sun, if on time, would rise at 6:00 A.M. local time.)

Sunrise on standard meridian, sun on time . . . . 6:00   A.M.

Correction for longitude . . . . _____

Corrected time . . . . _____

Correction for equation of time . . . . _____

Corrected time of sunrise . . . . _____ Ans.

Group F

TIDES

Text References

Strahler, 1969, *Physical Geography*, 3rd Edition Chapter 6, pp. 97–109.
Strahler, 1970, *Introduction to Physical Geography, 2nd Edition,* Chapter 24, pp. 358–360.

Data Tables (Source: H. S. Marmer, from U. S. Coast & Geodetic Survey)

F-1 San Francisco, California—October 18

Hour	Height (Feet)	Hour	Height (Feet)
12 midnight	0.0	1 P.M.	−0.3
1 A.M.	−1.5	2 P.M.	−1.5
2 A.M.	−2.3	3 P.M.	−2.4
3 A.M.	−2.6	4 P.M.	−2.5
4 A.M.	−2.3	5 P.M.	−1.9
5 A.M.	−1.5	6 P.M.	−1.0
6 A.M.	−0.3	7 P.M.	0.1
7 A.M.	0.8	8 P.M.	1.2
8 A.M.	2.0	9 P.M.	2.0
9 A.M.	2.6	10 P.M.	2.3
10 A.M.	2.8	11 P.M.	2.2
11 A.M.	2.3	12 midnight	1.2
12 noon	1.2		

F-2 San Francisco, California—October 24

Hour	Height (Feet)	Hour	Height (Feet)
12 midnight	0.0	1 P.M.	−2.6
1 A.M.	−0.5	2 P.M.	−3.3
2 A.M.	−0.5	3 P.M.	−3.3
3 A.M.	−0.3	4 P.M.	−2.9
4 A.M.	0.5	5 P.M.	−1.8
5 A.M.	1.4	6 P.M.	−0.9
6 A.M.	2.2	7 P.M.	0.1
7 A.M.	2.7	8 P.M.	1.1
8 A.M.	2.8	9 P.M.	1.6
9 A.M.	2.3	10 P.M.	1.8
10 A.M.	1.3	11 P.M.	1.5
11 A.M.	−0.2	12 midnight	0.9
12 noon	−1.5		

F-3 St. Michael, Alaska

First Day		Second Day	
Hour	Height (Feet)	Hour	Height (Feet)
0	1.0	0	1.1
2	2.0	2	2.3
4	2.3	4	3.0
6	1.7	6	2.9
8	0.4	8	1.9
10	−0.5	10	0.4
12 noon	−1.2	12 noon	−0.5
14	−1.6	14	−1.3
16	−1.8	16	−1.8
18	−1.8	18	−2.2
20	−1.6	20	−2.2
22	−0.5	22	−1.8
24	1.1	24	−0.5

Exercise F-1 TIDE CURVE FOR SAN FRANCISCO, CALIFORNIA, OCTOBER 18

Refer to hourly tide data for San Francisco, October 18, on page 61. On the blank graph below, plot the height of water for each hour and connect the points with a smooth curve.

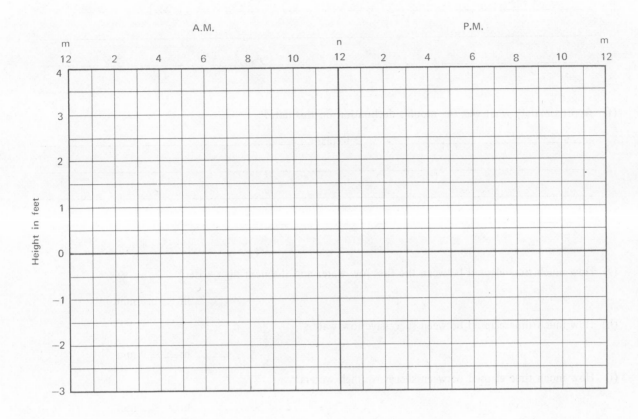

QUESTIONS

(a) What type of tide curve is illustrated by the graph you have completed?

_____

_____

(b) Determine as closely as you can the heights of the two high waters and the two low waters (give to nearest 1/10 ft).

First high water _____ ft   First low water _____ ft

Second high water _____ ft   Second low water _____ ft

(c) What were the ranges between successive low and high waters?

Range from first low to first high water _____ ft

Range from second low to second high water _____ ft

(Continue on reverse side of page)

$\mathbf{F_1}$ (d) Did both low waters reach the same mark? _____

(e) Did both high waters reach the same mark? _____

If either answer is "No" explain below.

_____

_____

_____

_____

_____

_____

(f) Approximately what was the moon's declination on this date?

_____ Explain. _____

_____

_____

_____

(g) How much time elapsed between the first low water and the next high water?

_____ hr _____ min

(h) How much time elapsed between successive low waters?

_____ hr _____ min

(i) How much time elapsed between successive high waters?

_____ hr _____ min

Optional Project

Fit a system of lunar hours to the tide curve of San Francisco. First draw vertical lines through the two high-water points. Make sure that the time elapsed between these points is 12 hr 25 min (12.42 hr). Then divide the intervening distance into six equal parts, each part representing one lunar hour. Extend the lunar hour system to cover the remainder of the graph. Number the lunar hours, starting with "zero" at the first midtide point.

Plot a sine curve fitted to the lunar hour system, in phase with the tide curve. Let the amplitude of the tide curve be 5.0 ft. Use the zero height level of the tide curve for the zero value of the sine curve. The crest of the sine wave will thus rise to +2.5 ft and will fall to a trough at −2.5 ft. Plot one point for each lunar hour and connect with a smooth curve.

(Reference: Strahler, 1969, *Physical Geography, 3rd Edition.* See p. 666 and Figure A IV.1.)

Exercise F-2 TIDE CURVE FOR SAN FRANCISCO, CALIFORNIA, OCTOBER 24

Refer to hourly tide data for San Francisco, October 24, page 61. On the blank graph below, plot the tide curve, as in Exercise F-1.

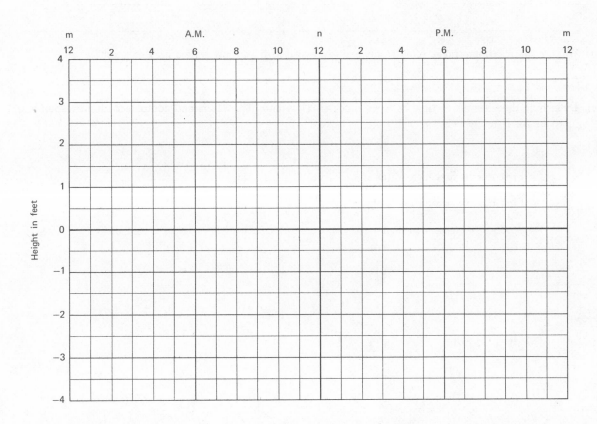

QUESTIONS

(a) What type of tide curve is illustrated by the graph you have completed?

_____

_____

_____

(b) Determine the heights and times of occurrence of each low water and each high water. (Read to nearest 1/10 ft and to 10 min.)

First low water _____ ft _____ hr

First high water _____ ft _____ hr

Second low water _____ ft _____ hr

Second high water _____ ft _____ hr

(Continue on reverse side of page)

F
2

(c) Explain why the first high water is higher than the second; the second low water lower than the first. (Note date and compare with Exercise F-1)

_____

_____

_____

_____

_____

_____

(d) What is the maximum range of tide between successive high and low waters on this graph?

_____ ft

(e) Determine the intervals of time between successive low and high waters and compare with corresponding intervals for Exercise F-1.

	Ex. F-2	Ex. F-1
First low to first high water	_____ hr	_____ hr
First high to second low water	_____ hr	_____ hr
Second low to second high water	_____ hr	_____ hr

Exercise F-3 TIDE CURVE FOR ST. MICHAEL, ALASKA

Refer to data for St. Michael on page 61. Note that heights are given for every second hour and that a two-day period is covered. On the blank graph below, plot the tide curve, as in Exercise F-1.

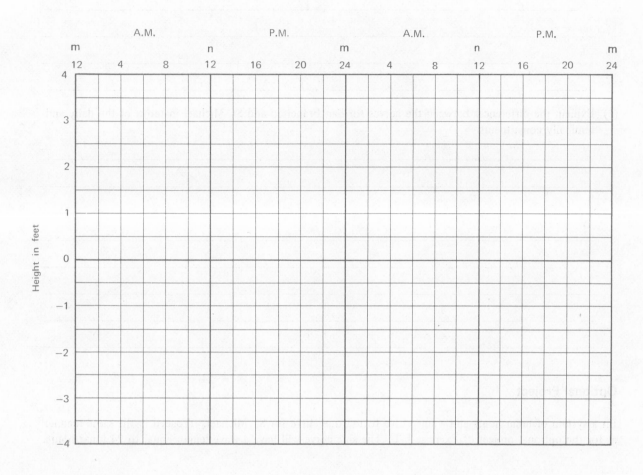

QUESTIONS

(a) What type of tide curve is represented by the graph you have drawn?

_____

_____

_____

(b) What interval of time elapsed between successive high waters?

Time of first high water   _____ (to nearest 10 min)

Time of second high water _____

Elapsed time   _____ hr

(Continue on reverse side of page)

F
3

(c) What interval of time elapsed between successive low waters?

Time of first low water   _____ (to nearest 10 min)

Time of second low water   _____

Elapsed time   _____ hr

(d) How does this tide period compare with that of San Francisco in Exercises F-1 and F-2?

_____

_____

_____

_____

(e) Explain the differences between the curves for San Francisco and St. Michael in terms of the daily and semidaily constituents.

_____

_____

_____

_____

_____

_____

_____

Optional Project

Fit a system of lunar hours and a sine curve to the tide curve for St. Michael. Proceed in the same manner as for the optional project of Exercise F-1. The sine curve will have a wave length equal to 24 lunar hours.

Exercise F-4 NEAP AND SPRING TIDES

The table below lists heights of successive high and low waters at Boston, Massachusetts for January, 1961. (Data from U. S. Coast & Geodetic Survey, *Tide Tables for 1961*.)

Date	Low	High
Jan. 1	0.5	
		10.1
	−0.5	
		8.8
Jan. 2	0.5	
		10.1
	−0.5	
		8.9
Jan. 3	0.5	
		10.1
	−0.5	
Jan. 4		8.9
	0.5	
		10.0
	−0.4	
Jan. 5		8.9
	0.6	
		9.8
	−0.3	
Jan. 6		8.9
	0.7	
		9.5
	−0.2	
Jan. 7		8.9
	0.7	
		9.3
	0.0	
Jan. 8		8.9
	0.8	
		9.0
	0.2	
Jan. 9		9.0
	0.8	
		8.8
	0.3	
Jan. 10		9.1
	0.6	
		8.7
	0.4	
Jan. 11		9.4
	0.4	
		8.7
	0.3	
Jan. 12		9.7
	0.0	
		8.8
	0.1	
Jan. 13		10.2
	−0.5	
		9.1

Date	Low	High
Jan. 14	−0.2	
		10.8
	−1.1	
		9.5
Jan. 15	−0.6	
		11.3
	−1.6	
		10.0
Jan. 16	−1.0	
		11.7
	−2.0	
		10.4
Jan. 17	−1.3	
		11.9
	−2.2	
		10.6
Jan. 18	−1.4	
		11.9
	−2.3	
		10.7
Jan. 19	−1.4	
		11.7
	−2.1	
		10.6
Jan. 20	−1.2	
		11.2
	−1.7	
		10.5
Jan. 21	−0.9	
		10.6
	−1.2	
		10.2
Jan. 22	−0.5	
		9.9
	−0.6	
		9.8
Jan. 23	−0.1	
		9.3
	0.0	
		9.6
Jan. 24	0.3	
		8.7
	0.5	
		9.4
Jan. 25	0.5	
		8.4
	0.8	
		9.3
Jan. 26	0.5	
		8.2

Date	Low	High
Jan. 27	0.9	
		9.3
	0.4	
		8.2
Jan. 28	1.0	
		9.5
	0.2	
		8.3
Jan. 29	0.9	
		9.6
	0.0	
		8.5
Jan. 30	0.8	
		9.7
	−0.2	
		8.7
Jan. 31	0.6	
		9.8
	−0.3	
		8.9
Feb. 1	0.5	
		9.9
	−0.4	

MOON DATA

Phases:	Day	Hour	Symbol
Full	Jan. 1	18	○
3rd 1/4	9	22	◑
New	16	16½	●
1st 1/4	23	11	◐
Full	31	14	○
Apogee	3	8	A
Perigee	16	18	P
Apogee	30	8	A
Declination:			
Max. North	1	7	N
Zero	8	20	E
Max. South	15	8	S
Zero	21	10	E
Max. North	28	14	N
Zero	Feb. 5	2	E

Exercise F-4 NEAP AND SPRING TIDES

On the graph below, plot high and low waters from the table on page 69. As indicated on the graph, find the point precisely and encircle it for easy visibility. Connect the higher high-water points by a smooth curve; the lower high-water points by a second curve. Draw two similar curves for the low waters. Enter the symbols for moon's phase, apogee or perigee, and declination near the top of the graph, locating each at the precise date of occurrence.

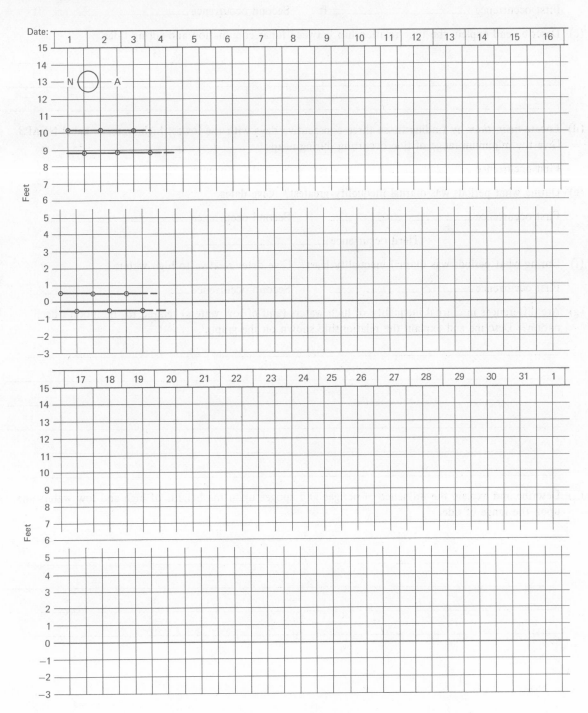

F
4
QUESTIONS

(a) Compute the length of the synodic month. (First full moon to second full moon.)

Ans._____

(b) Locate *spring tides* by finding those three consecutive days showing the highest high waters. Label SPRINGS. Give the maximum range of tide occurring during springs. (Greatest difference between one low water and the next high water, or vice versa.)

First occurrence _____ ft   Second occurrence _____ ft

(c) Describe and explain the time relationship between lunar conjunction and spring tides.

_____

_____

_____

(d) Locate *neap tides* by finding those three consecutive days with the lowest high waters. Label NEAPS. Give the minimum range of tide occurring during neaps.

First occurrence _____ ft   Second occurrence _____ ft

(e) During what periods was diurnal inequality greatest? Give dates.

First occurrence _____   Second occurrence _____

Third occurrence _____

(f) During what periods was diurnal inequality least? Give dates relative to high waters.

First occurrence _____   Second occurrence _____

(g) Are differences in diurnal inequality of high waters (and of low waters) related to the moon's declination? Describe and explain the relationship shown on the graph.

_____

_____

_____

_____

_____

_____

(h) Describe and explain the influence of perigee and apogee upon the heights of high and low waters and upon the range of tide.

_____

_____

_____

_____

_____

_____

_____

Group G

VERTICAL DISTRIBUTION OF AIR TEMPERATURE AND PRESSURE

Text References

Strahler, 1969, *Physical Geography, 3rd Edition* Chapter 7, pp. 113–123.
Strahler, 1970, *Introduction to Physical Geography, 2nd Edition*, Chapter 3, pp. 43–46.

Pressure-Altitude Table. U. S. Standard Atmosphere

Pressure mb	Altitude m	Pressure in.	Altitude ft
400	7,425	11.80	24,370
500	5,643	14.75	18,520
600	4,186	17.70	13,740
700	2,955	20.65	9,700
800	1,889	23.63	6,200
900	984	26.58	3,112
1000	106	29.53	348
1013	0	29.92	0

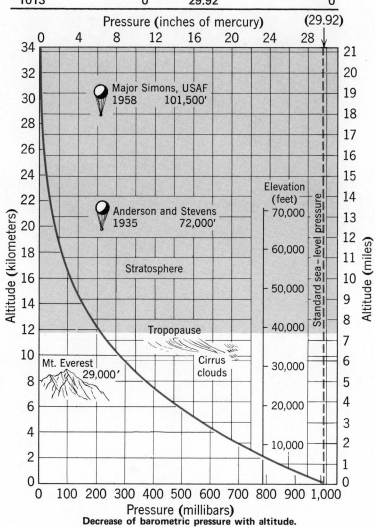

Decrease of barometric pressure with altitude.

Name_____ Date_____
Course No._____ Section_____

G1, 2

Exercise G-1 LAPSE RATE AND TROPOPAUSE IN MIDDLE LATITUDES

At Chicago, Illinois, on a day in mid-April, the surface air temperature measures 50°F. A vertical sounding of the atmosphere by balloon reveals a nearly constant temperature-lapse rate of 3.6F° per 1000 ft. At the tropopause a temperature of −58°F is reported. (Assume the elevation of Chicago to be sea level.)

(a) Calculate the altitude of the tropopause (show computations).

Ans. _____ ft

(b) Convert your answer for (a) into kilometers.

Ans. _____ km

(c) On the graph on page 76, plot the lapse rate curve and draw a horizontal line at the tropopause. Label fully.

Exercise G-2 LAPSE RATE AND TROPOPAUSE NEAR THE EQUATOR

Nauru Island is located in mid-Pacific, close to the Equator. On the same day that observations are being made at Chicago, a similar sounding is being made at Nauru. Here the sea-level temperature is 30°C and the lapse rate is constant at 6.6C° per km. The tropopause is encountered at 16.8 km.

(a) Calculate the air temperature at the tropopause (show computations).

Ans. _____ °C

(b) Convert your answer to degrees Fahrenheit.

Ans. _____ °F

(c) Construct scales in units of kilometers and degrees Centigrade for the graph on page 76. Plot the data of this exercise on the graph. Draw a horizontal line at the tropopause. Label scales, lapse rate curve, and tropopause.

G1, 2

Graph to accompany Exercises G-1 and G-2.

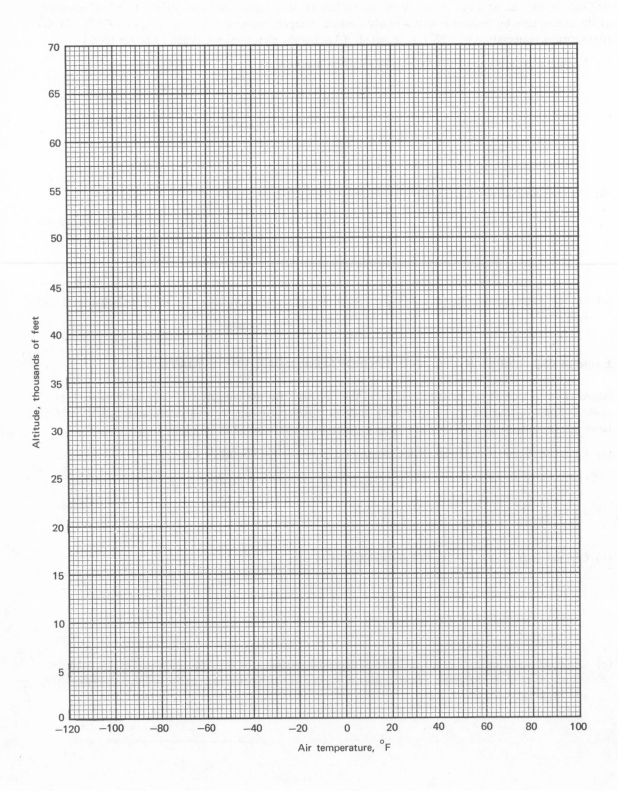

Exercise G-3 PRESSURE VERSUS ALTITUDE

The table on page 73 gives figures for barometric pressure at various altitudes, according to standards used by the U. S. Weather Bureau for correcting barometric readings to sea level equivalents. (Refer to questions on reverse side of this page.)

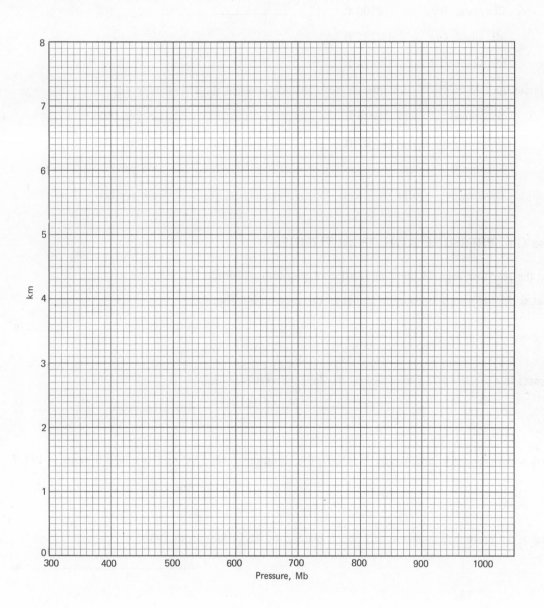

km

Pressure, Mb

QUESTIONS

Plot the data from the table on page 73 on the graph on page 77. Connect the points with a smooth curve. Prepare equivalent scales in inches and feet and mark them on the upper edge and right-hand edge of the graph. Plot the points for inches-feet equivalents from the table. These points should fall on the line previously drawn.

(a) Using the graph, estimate the standard barometric pressure for each of the following places:

Canton, Ohio   1030 ft   _____

Las Vegas, Nevada   2030 ft   _____

Cheyenne, Wyo.   6100 ft   _____

Mt. Hood, Ore.   11,235 ft   _____

Mr. Whitney, Calif.   14,494 ft   _____

(b) Estimate the rate of decrease of pressure with altitude between the following levels:

Between 0   and   1000 ft: _____ in per 1000 ft

Between 10,000 and 11,000 ft: _____ in per 1000 ft

Between 0   and   1 km: _____ mb per km.

Between 6   and   7 km: _____ mb per km.

Exercise G-4 PRESSURE AT HIGH ALTITUDES

Refer to the graph on page 73, showing relation of pressure to altitude.

(a) What is the barometric pressure in inches of mercury on Mt. Everest?

Ans. _____ in

Express this pressure as a percentage of standard sea-level pressure.

Ans. _____ %

(b) What is the pressure in millibars at 72,000 ft, the elevation reached by Anderson and Stevens in 1935?

Ans. _____ mb

(c) What is the pressure in inches at 101,500 ft reached by Major Simons in 1958?

Ans. _____ in.

Group H

SOLAR RADIATION AND AIR TEMPERATURE

Text References

Strahler, 1969, *Physical Geography, 3rd Edition*, Chapter 8, pp. 125–149.
Strahler, 1970, *Introduction to Physical Geography, 2nd Edition*, Chapter 4, pp. 51–70.

ANGOT'S INSOLATION TABLE
(To accompany Exercise H-2.)

Insolation received during each month of the year at various latitudes, assuming a completely transparent atmosphere. The value of one unit used in this table is 889 gram calories per square centimeter, which is the quantity of radiation received at the equator in one day at equinox. (Data from Brunt, *Physical and Dynamical Meteorology*, Cambridge University Press, 1939.)

Latitude		Jan.	Feb.	Mar.	Apr.	May	Jun.	Jul.	Aug.	Sep.	Oct.	Nov.	Dec.	Total for year
	90	...	...	1.9	17.5	31.5	36.4	32.9	21.1	4.6	...	...	...	145.9
	80	...	0.1	5.0	17.5	30.5	35.8	32.4	20.9	7.4	0.6	...	...	150.2
°N	60	3.0	7.4	14.8	23.2	30.2	33.2	31.1	24.9	16.7	9.0	3.8	1.9	199.2
	40	12.5	17.0	23.1	28.6	32.4	33.8	32.8	29.4	24.3	18.4	13.4	11.1	276.8
	20	22.0	25.1	28.6	30.9	31.8	32.0	31.8	30.9	28.9	25.8	22.5	20.9	331.2
Equator		29.4	30.4	30.6	29.6	28.0	27.1	27.6	28.6	30.1	30.2	29.5	28.9	350.0
	20	33.8	32.2	29.0	24.9	21.2	19.6	20.5	23.7	27.7	31.1	33.3	34.1	331.1
	40	34.8	30.4	23.9	17.4	12.5	10.4	11.6	15.8	21.9	28.5	33.6	36.0	276.8
°S	60	33.0	25.3	16.0	8.1	3.3	1.7	2.7	6.5	13.6	22.6	31.1	38.1	199.2
	80	34.2	20.5	6.3	0.3	...	...	...	...	3.8	16.0	31.0	38.1	150.2
	90	34.7	20.7	3.2	...	...	...	...	...	1.0	15.6	31.5	38.7	145.4

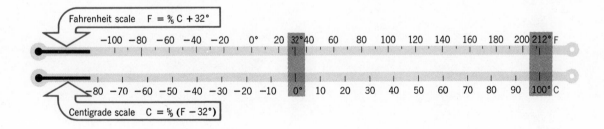

Conversion of Fahrenheit to Centigrade (Celsius) and vice versa.

Exercise H-1 INSOLATION AND LATITUDE

Using the diagrams below, calculate the intensity of insolation upon a horizontal surface at noon at equinox for various latitudes. Intensity is assumed to be 100% at the equator. It is assumed that no atmosphere exists. Use either the trigonometric method or the direct measurement method based upon constructed triangles. The problem is solved for 45° latitude.

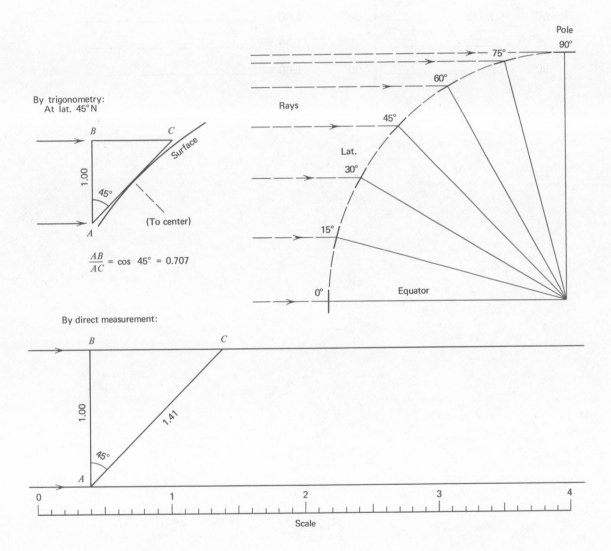

By trigonometry:
At lat. 45°N

$$\frac{AB}{AC} = \cos\ 45° = 0.707$$

By direct measurement:

(Enter answers in data table on reverse side of page)

H₁

Exercise H-1. (Table of answers)

Trigonometry			Direct measurement				
Lat.	Cos lat.	× 100	Lat	AB	AC	$\dfrac{AB}{AC}$	× 100
0°	1.000	100%	0°	1.00	1.00	1.00	100%
15°	_____	_____	15°	1.00	_____	_____	_____
30°	_____	_____	30°	1.00	_____	_____	_____
45°	0.707	70.7%	45°	1.00	1.41	0.707	70.7%
60°	_____	_____	60°	1.00	_____	_____	_____
75°	_____	_____	75°	1.00	_____	_____	_____
90°	_____	_____	90°	1.00	_____	_____	_____

Exercise H-2 ANNUAL CYCLE OF INSOLATION

On the upper of the two graphs on page 84, plot the sun's declination at ten-day intervals throughout the year; use the data on page 55. Draw a smooth curve through the points.

On the lower graph, plot monthly insolation totals for 0° (equator), 20°N, 40°S, 60°N, and 90°N (north pole). Use the data of Angot's insolation table on page 79. Each monthly total should be shown as a point in the middle of the month, as shown by the partially completed graph for 60°N. Connect the points with a smooth curve. Use a different color for each latitude.

QUESTIONS

(a) Compare the insolation curves with the annual curve of the sun's declination. Compare times of maximum and minimum values at 60°N and 40°S. Explain how the two sets of data are related.

_____

_____

_____

_____

_____

_____

(b) Explain how the maxima and minima of insolation at the equator are related to the curve of the sun's declination.

_____

_____

_____

(c) What disadvantage lies in the use of calendar months for analysis of the yearly cycle of insolation? Cite specific figures from Angot's table.

_____

_____

_____

_____

_____

(d) Why does the south pole receive more insolation in January than the north pole receives in July?

_____

_____

_____

_____

H₂

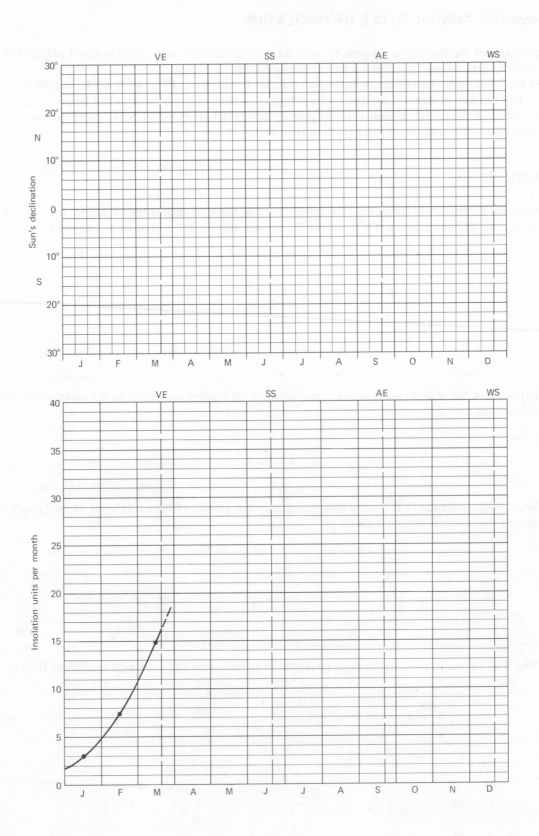

84

Exercise H-3 ANNUAL CYCLE OF AIR TEMPERATURE

The figures given below are monthly mean air temperatures, °F, for two stations, one in the southern hemisphere, one in the northern. On the blank graph below, plot each monthly mean value as a point. Connect the points with a smooth curve. Because monthly values are rounded to the nearest one-half degree, points may lie to one side or the other of your fitted curve.

	J	F	M	A	M	J	J	A	S	O	N	D
Auckland, N. Z., 37°S lat.	66.5	66.5	63.0	61.5	56.5	53.0	53.0	52.0	54.5	57.5	60.0	63.5
Churchill, Manitoba, Can., 59°N lat.	−19.0	−16.5	−6.0	14.0	30.0	43.0	53.5	52.5	41.5	27.0	5.5	−11.0

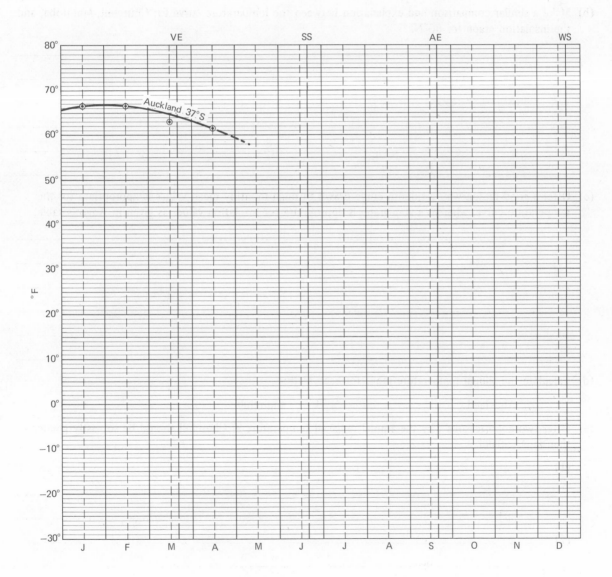

(Continue with questions on the reverse side of this page)

H₃

QUESTIONS

(a) Compare the temperature curve of Auckland, N. Z., with the insolation graph for 40°S, which you drew on page 84. Describe and explain the relationship between months of maximum and minimum temperatures and months of maximum and minimum insolation.

_____

_____

_____

_____

_____

_____

(b) Make a similar comparison and explanation between the temperature curve for Churchill, Manitoba, and the insolation graph for 60°N.

_____

_____

_____

_____

_____

(c) Offer a good reason why a smooth curve drawn through monthly mean values is appropriate for the temperature curve, whereas a step-graph is appropriate for insolation values as given in Angot's table.

_____

_____

_____

_____

_____

_____

(d) Calculate the annual temperature range for each station.

        Auckland _____ F°   Churchill _____ F°

(e) Offer two good reasons why the annual range of temperature at Churchill should be so vastly greater than at Auckland.

(1) _____

_____

_____

(2) _____

_____

_____

Exercise H-4 CONVERSION OF TEMPERATURE SCALES

Use the formulas on page 79 for conversion of Fahrenheit temperatures to Centigrade (Celsius) and vice versa. Show your computations. Use the graphic comparison scale on page 79 for rough check only.

(a) Convert the following Fahrenheit temperatures to Centigrade:

$$32°F \quad \text{_____} °C$$

$$0°F \quad \text{_____} °C$$

$$90°F \quad \text{_____} °C$$

$$-22°F \quad \text{_____} °C$$

(b) Convert the following Centigrade temperatures to Fahrenheit:

$$0°C \quad \text{_____} °F$$

$$100°C \quad \text{_____} °F$$

$$11°C \quad \text{_____} °F$$

$$-40°C \quad \text{_____} °F$$

Exercise H-5 DRAWING OF ISOTHERMS

On the reverse side of this page is a map of a portion of the United States on which air temperatures in degrees Fahrenheit have been plotted. Readings were taken at 1:30 A.M., E.S.T. at U. S. Weather Bureau observing stations. The date is early in May. The 32° (freezing) isotherm is shown. Draw isotherms for every 5°.

Method of drawing isotherms is illustrated by a portion of the 40° isotherm. Begin with a station numbered "40." Draw the line so as to pass between pairs of adjacent numbers, one of which is higher than 40, the other less than 40. Space the distance between the two numbers in proportion to the value of the number 40 with respect to the higher and lower numbers. If the numbers on either side are 35 and 45, the 40° isotherm will pass midway between them. Label each isotherm.

Use a soft lead pencil and draw the isotherms very lightly at first. When the map is completed, adjust the lines to form smooth sweeping curves. Note that isotherms may not intersect one another. They may, however, form closed loops surrounding centers of high or low temperatures.

H₅ Isotherm map to accompany Exercise H-5

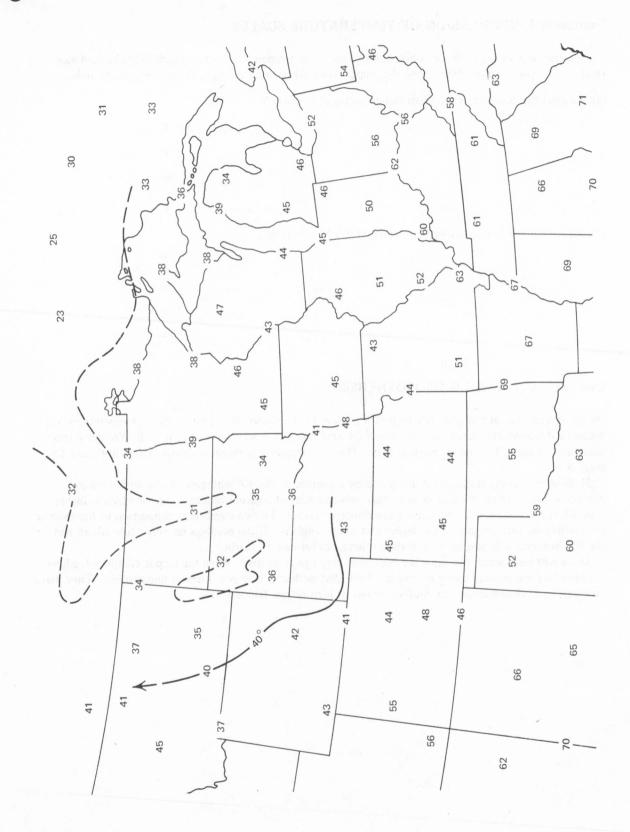

Exercise H-6 DAILY CYCLE OF NET RADIATION AND AIR TEMPERATURE

Given below are data for net all-wave radiation at the ground and air temperature for a station in the middle-western United States at about latitude 40°N on a day in mid-August. Sunrise occurred at 5:15 A.M.; sunset about 6:50 P.M., local time. Plot the data on the graph below. Answer questions on reverse side of this page.

	Mid-night	2	4	A.M. 6	8	10	Noon 12	2	4	P.M. 6	8	10	Mid-night
Net All-Wave Radiation, ly/hr	−5	−5	−5	−2	+25	+41	+52	+45	+24	−1	−5	−5	−5
Air Temperature, °C	14	13	12.5	12	15	22	25.5	27	26.5	23	19	16.5	14

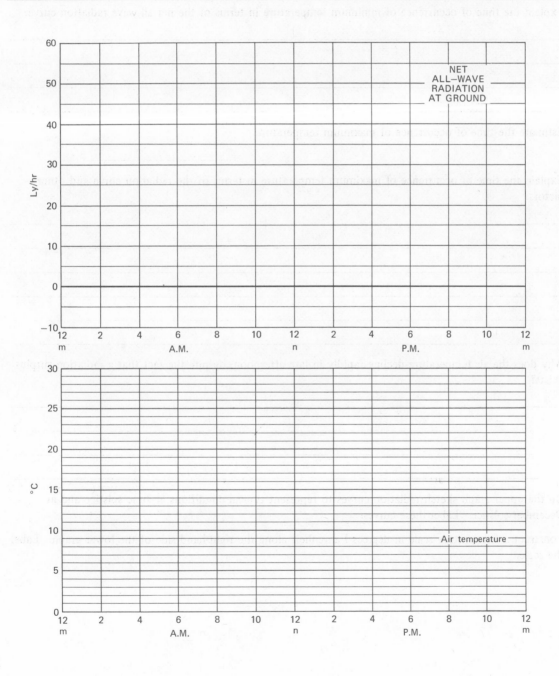

QUESTIONS

(a) Using color pencils, color *red* the areas of radiation deficit on the upper graph. Color *blue* the area of surplus. Label these areas.

Estimate the time at which deficit changed to surplus:

_____ A.M.

Estimate the time at which surplus changed to deficit:

_____ P.M.

(b) Estimate the time of occurrence of minimum temperature on the lower graph:

_____ A.M.

Explain the time of occurrence of minimum temperature in terms of the net all-wave radiation curve.

_____

_____

_____

_____

(c) Estimate the time of occurrence of maximum temperature.

_____ P.M.

Explain the time of occurrence of maximum temperature in terms of the radiation curve and other factors.

_____

_____

_____

_____

_____

_____

(d) Why does the air temperature decline rapidly in late afternoon, despite the fact that a radiation surplus exists?

_____

_____

_____

_____

(e) On the upper graph sketch radiation curves to represent typical conditions at June solstice and at December solstice. Label these curves.

(f) Construct a temperature scale in degrees Fahrenheit along the right-hand side of the lower graph. Label the scale.

Group I

BAROMETRIC PRESSURE AND WINDS

Text References

Strahler, 1969, *Physical Geography, 3rd Edition,* Chapter 9, pp. 168.
Strahler, 1970, *Introduction to Physical Geography, 2nd Edition,* Chapter 5, pp. 73–86.

Scale for conversion of millibars to inches (For use in Exercise I-1.)

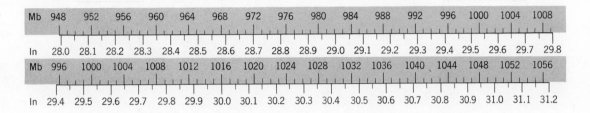

1.0 in. (mercury) = 33.87 mb = 2.54 mm (mercury)
1.0 mb = 0.029 in. = 0.75 mm
1.0 mm = 0.039 in. = 1.333 mb

Wind arrows used on U. S. Weather Bureau maps (For use in Exercise I-2)

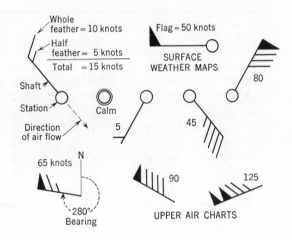

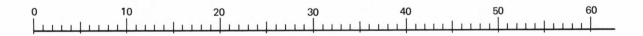

Wind rose used on U. S. Navy Oceanographic Office Pilot Charts. (For use in Exercise I-3.)

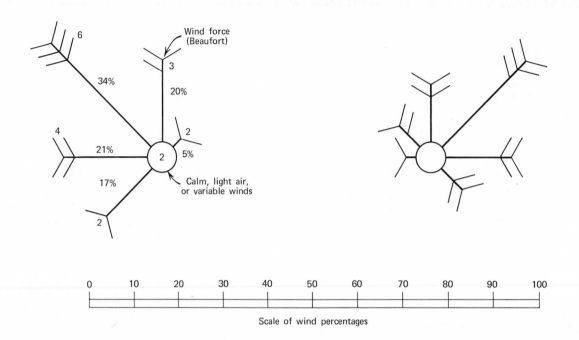

Scale of wind percentages

Wind Rose Data for Exercise I-4

	A %	A Force	B %	B Force	C %	C Force	D %	D Force
N	6	2	7	3	15	2	1	4
NE	12	3	4	4	14	3	64	4
E	11	2	4	4	9	3	33	4
SE	9	3	5	4	13	3	2	3
S	17	3	16	4	19	3	0	0
SW	17	3	24	4	11	3	0	0
W	11	3	24	5	4	2	0	0
NW	9	3	15	4	4	2	0	0
Calms	8	—	1	—	11	—	0	—

Exercise I-1 BAROMETRIC PRESSURE CONVERSIONS

Barometric pressure readings are given below in one of three units of measurement: inches, millimeters, or millibars. Using the conversion data on page 91, convert the given figure into the other two units.

Inches	Millimeters	Millibars
30.12	_____	_____
_____	710	_____
_____	_____	1006
29.60	_____	_____
_____	758	_____
_____	_____	500

Exercise I-2 WIND ARROWS

Using the U. S. Weather Bureau system illustrated on page 91, construct wind arrows to the following specifications. Draw the shaft at the correct bearing angle with respect to the coordinates drawn below.

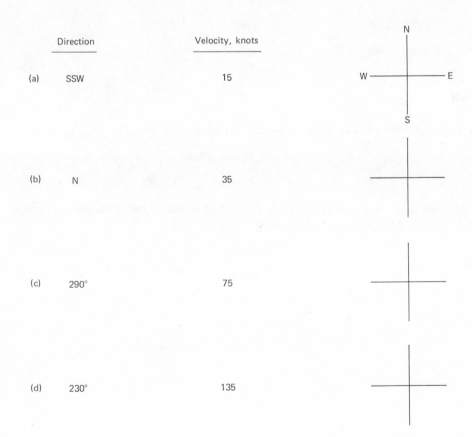

	Direction	Velocity, knots
(a)	SSW	15
(b)	N	35
(c)	290°	75
(d)	230°	135

I 3 Exercise I-3 READING THE WIND ROSE

Refer to the right-hand wind rose on page 92. Using the scale below the rose, estimate the percentages of time during which the wind blows from each of the sectors of the rose. Measure shaft length from the center of the circle. Total the percentages and subtract from 100 in order to determine the percentage of light air and calm.

Enter your data below:

Sector	Percent of Time	Force
N	_____	_____
NE	_____	_____
E	_____	_____
SE	_____	_____
S	_____	_____
SW	_____	_____
W	_____	_____
NW	_____	_____
Total percent	_____	
Percent calms	_____	

QUESTIONS

(a) Identify the wind belt from which the above data are taken. Estimate the latitude.

Name of belt _____

Latitude _____ ° _____

(b) Examine the left-hand wind rose on page 92, on which percentages and wind force are labeled. From what wind belt is this rose taken? Estimate the latitude.

Name of belt _____

Latitude _____ ° _____

Exercise I-4 REPRESENTATIVE WIND ROSES FOR WIND BELTS

On the blank wind roses below, and on the opposite side of this page, construct wind roses for the four localities for which data are given on page 92. The scale of percentages printed at the bottom of page 91 may be cut off and used directly in plotting. After the wind rose is completed, identify the wind belt from which it comes and label accordingly.

A _____

B _____

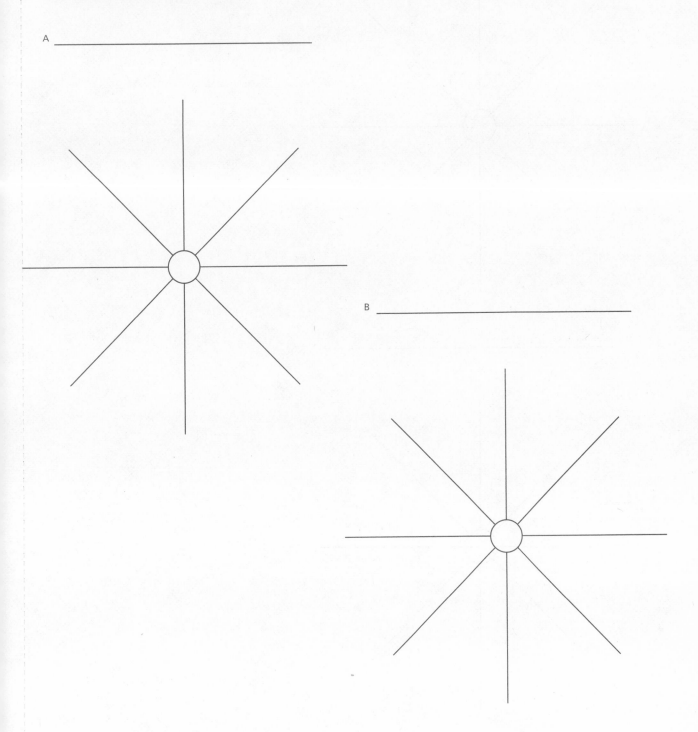

4 **Exercise I-4** *(continued)*

C

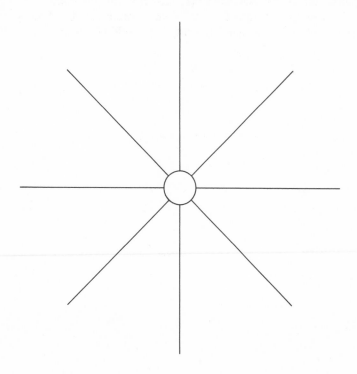

D

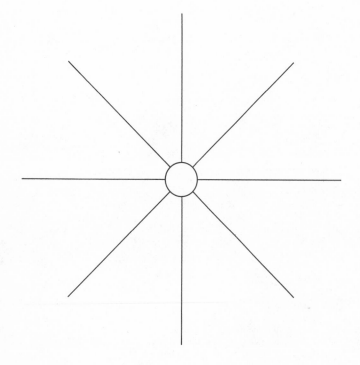

Exercise I-5 UPPER-AIR WINDS

The map below shows barometric pressure conditions at high levels by means of contours drawn upon the 500-millibar pressure surface. Contours are labeled in thousands of feet. The map shows conditions at 7:00 P.M., E.S.T. on a day in early April. (Data of U. S. Weather Bureau.)

Treating the contours as if they were isobars, drawn numerous arrow points on the contours to show the direction of air motion. Draw broad, sweeping arrows to show the probable position of the jet stream in two places on the map. Label a *cyclone*; label an *anticyclone*.

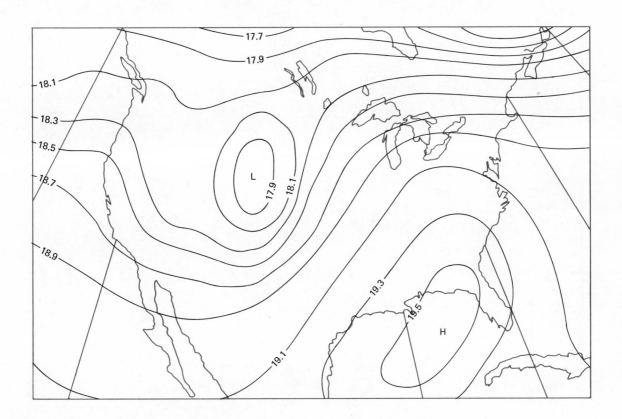

Exercise I-6 ISOBARS ON SURFACE WEATHER MAP

On the reverse side of this page is a weather map showing barometric pressures observed simultaneously at many U. S. Weather Bureau observing stations. Pressures are in millibars. Only the last two digits are given. Hence, *16* designates *1016*; *96* designates *996*. Station location is shown by a dot beside the numeral.

Draw isobars for the entire map, using an interval of 4 mb. Isobars should run thus: 992, 996, 1000, 1004, 1008, 1012, 1016, 1020, 1024, 1028. Label isobars. Label lows and highs. Use pencil lightly at first; then draw final lines as smooth flowing curves, except where abrupt pressure changes (fronts) occur. Finally, draw many short, straight arrows across the isobars to show the directions of surface winds.

I6

Isobaric map to accompany Exercise I-6

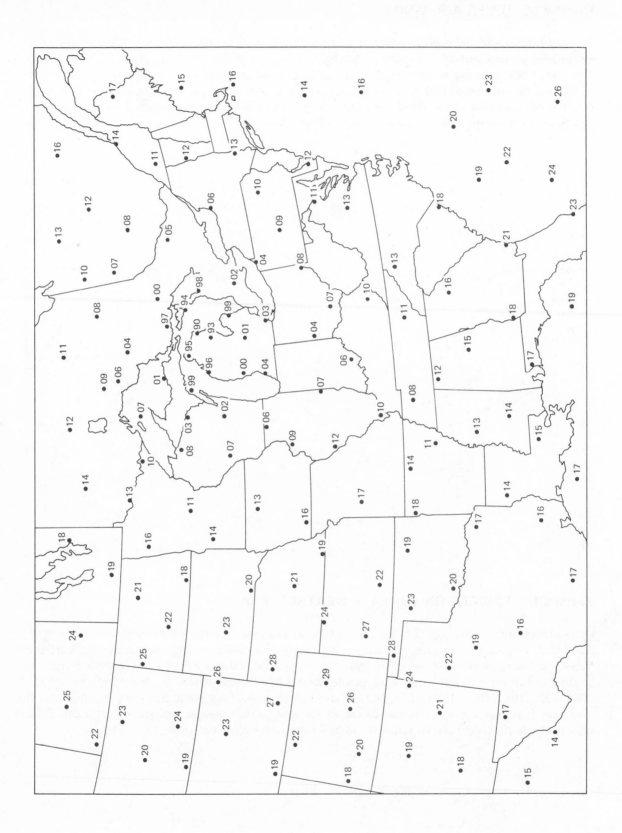

Group J

J

ATMOSPHERIC MOISTURE AND PRECIPITATION

Text References

Strahler, 1969, *Physical Geography, 3rd Edition*, Chapter 11, pp. 181–197.
Strahler, 1970, *Introduction to Physical Geography, 2nd Edition*, Chapter 6, pp. 91–104.

PSYCHROMETRIC TABLES (Exercise J-1.)

Table A. Relative Humidity, per cent. Temperatures in °F

Air Temperature	Dry Bulb Minus Wet Bulb																													
---	1	2	3	4	5	6	7	8	9	10	11	12	13	14	15	16	17	18	19	20	21	22	23	24	25	26	27	28	29	30
0	67	33	1																											
5	73	46	20																											
10	78	56	34	13																										
15	82	64	46	29	11																									
20	85	70	55	40	26	12																								
25	87	74	62	49	37	25	13	1																						
30	89	78	67	56	46	36	26	16	6																					
35	91	81	72	63	54	45	36	27	19	10	2																			
40	92	83	75	68	60	52	45	37	29	22	15	7																		
45	93	86	78	71	64	57	51	44	38	31	25	18	12	6																
50	93	87	80	74	67	61	55	49	43	38	32	27	21	16	10	5														
55	94	88	82	76	70	65	59	54	49	43	38	33	28	23	19	14	9	5												
60	94	89	83	78	73	68	63	58	53	48	43	39	34	30	26	21	17	13	9	5	1									
65	95	90	85	80	75	70	66	61	56	52	48	44	39	35	31	27	24	20	16	12	9	5	2							
70	95	90	86	81	77	72	68	64	59	55	51	48	44	40	36	33	29	25	22	19	15	12	9	6	3					
75	96	91	86	82	78	74	70	66	62	58	54	51	47	44	40	37	34	30	27	24	21	18	15	12	9	7	4	1		
80	96	91	87	83	79	75	72	68	64	61	57	54	50	47	44	41	38	35	32	29	26	23	20	18	15	12	10	7	5	3
85	96	92	88	84	81	77	73	70	66	63	59	57	53	50	47	44	41	38	36	33	30	27	25	22	20	17	15	13	10	8
90	96	92	89	85	81	78	74	71	68	65	61	58	55	52	49	47	44	41	39	36	34	31	29	26	24	22	19	17	15	13
95	96	93	89	86	82	79	76	73	69	66	63	61	58	55	52	50	47	44	42	39	37	34	32	30	28	25	23	21	19	17
100	96	93	89	86	83	80	77	73	70	68	65	62	59	56	54	51	49	46	44	41	39	37	35	33	30	28	26	24	22	21
105	97	93	90	87	84	81	78	75	72	69	66	64	61	58	56	53	51	49	46	44	42	40	38	36	34	32	30	28	26	24
110	97	93	90	87	84	81	78	75	73	70	67	65	62	60	57	55	52	50	48	46	44	42	40	38	36	34	33	31	29	
115	97	94	91	88	85	82	79	76	74	71	69	66	64	61	59	57	54	52	50	48	46	44	42	40	38	36	34	33	31	29
120	97	94	91	88	85	82	80	77	74	72	69	67	65	62	60	58	55	53	51	49	47	45	43	41	40	38	36	34	33	31

Table B. Dew-Point Temperature, °F

Air Temperature	Vapor Pressure	Dry Bulb Minus Wet Bulb																												
---	---	1	2	3	4	5	6	7	8	9	10	11	12	13	14	15	16	17	18	19	20	21	22	23	24	25	26	27	28	29	30
0	.0383	−7	−20																												
5	.0491	−1	−9	−24																											
10	.0631	5	−2	−10	−27																										
15	.0810	11	6	0	−9	−26																									
20	.103	16	12	8	2	−7	−21																								
25	.130	22	19	15	10	5	−3	−15	−51																						
30	.164	27	25	21	18	14	8	2	−7	−25																					
35	.203	33	30	28	25	21	17	13	7	0	−11	−41																			
40	.247	38	35	33	30	28	25	21	18	13	7	−1	−14																		
45	.298	43	41	38	36	34	31	28	25	22	18	13	7	−1	−14																
50	.360	48	46	44	42	40	37	34	32	29	26	22	18	13	8	0	−13														
55	.432	53	51	50	48	45	43	41	38	36	33	30	27	24	20	15	9	1	−12	−59											
60	.517	58	57	55	53	51	49	47	45	43	40	38	35	32	29	25	21	17	11	4	−8	−36									
65	.616	63	62	60	59	57	55	53	51	49	47	45	42	40	37	34	31	27	24	19	14	7	−3	−22							
70	.732	69	67	65	64	62	61	59	57	55	53	51	49	47	44	42	39	36	33	30	26	22	17	11	2	−11					
75	.866	74	72	71	69	68	66	64	63	61	59	57	55	54	51	49	47	44	42	39	36	32	29	25	21	15	8	−2	−23		
80	1.022	79	77	76	74	73	72	70	68	67	65	63	62	60	58	56	54	52	50	47	44	42	39	36	32	28	24	20	13	6	−7
85	1.201	84	82	81	80	78	77	75	74	72	71	69	68	66	64	62	61	59	57	54	52	50	48	45	42	39	36	32	28	24	19
90	1.408	89	87	86	85	83	82	81	79	78	76	75	73	72	70	69	67	65	63	61	59	57	55	53	51	48	45	43	39	36	32
95	1.645	94	93	91	90	89	87	86	85	83	82	80	79	78	76	74	73	71	70	68	66	64	62	60	58	56	54	52	49	46	43
100	1.916	99	98	96	95	94	93	91	90	89	87	86	85	83	82	80	79	77	76	74	72	71	69	67	65	63	61	59	57	55	52
105	2.225	104	103	101	100	100	99	97	96	94	93	91	90	89	87	86	84	83	82	80	78	77	75	74	72	70	68	67	65	63	61
110	2.576	109	108	106	105	104	103	102	100	99	98	97	95	94	93	91	90	89	87	86	84	83	81	80	78	77	75	73	72	70	68
115	2.975	114	113	112	110	109	108	107	106	104	103	102	101	99	98	97	96	94	93	92	90	89	87	86	84	83	81	80	78	76	75
120	3.425	119	118	117	115	114	113	112	111	110	108	107	106	105	104	102	101	100	98	97	96	94	93	92	90	89	87	86	84	83	81

Exercise J-1 RELATIVE HUMIDITY AND DEW-POINT TEMPERATURE

(a) Use the tables on page 99 to determine relative humidity and dew-point temperature for each of the following pairs of temperature observations taken with the sling psychrometer:

		RH, %	Dew-point, °F
(1) Dry bulb	70°		
Wet bulb	50°		
(2) Dry bulb	95°		
Wet bulb	90°		
(3) Dry bulb	30°		
Wet bulb	22°		
(4) Dry bulb	105°		
Wet bulb	77°		

(b) Air having a temperature of 60°F and a relative humidity of 53% is heated to 90° without water vapor being added or removed. What is the relative humidity at 90°? (Use both tables on page 99)

Step 1   Difference in wet-bulb and dry-bulb
temperatures for 60° and 53% (Table A) .... _____°F

Step 2   Corresponding dew-point temperature
as shown in Table B .... _____°F

(Two additional steps required, using
Tables A and B) .... _____

Ans. _____%

(c) The same air described in (b) is cooled to 45° without gain or loss of water vapor. What is the relative humidity at 45°?

Ans. _____%

J_2

Exercise J-2 TEMPERATURE-HUMIDITY INDEX

Using the formula below, determine the THI of the four samples of air described in Exercise J-1 (a). Show computations.

Formula: $THI = 0.4 \, (T_{dry} + T_{wet}) + 15°$

(1)   Ans. _____

(2)   Ans. _____

(3)   Ans. _____

(4)   Ans. _____

Write a short statement evaluating each of the above samples in terms of comfort to human beings working indoors.

(1) _____

_____

(2) _____

_____

(3) _____

_____

(4) _____

_____

Optional Project

Obtain the use of a sling psychrometer. Take dry-bulb and wet-bulb temperature readings under a variety of weather conditions, including precipitation and fog. Obtain relative humidity and dew-point temperature readings at two-hour intervals throughout an entire day. Plot these values on a graph along with air temperature. Determine THI for a variety of weather conditions and relate these to personal comfort.

Exercise J-3 ADIABATIC COOLING

A mass of rising air has a temperature of 65°F at 1000 ft elevation. If the air temperature is decreasing at the dry adiabatic rate of 5.5 F° per 1000 ft, what will the temperature be at 4000 ft?

Ans. _____ °F

Assuming that this air initially has a dew-point temperature of 50°F, at what elevation will condensation set in? (Dew-point lapse rate is 1 F° per 1000 ft.)

Ans. _____ ft

Plot the data of this problem on the graph below. Label fully.

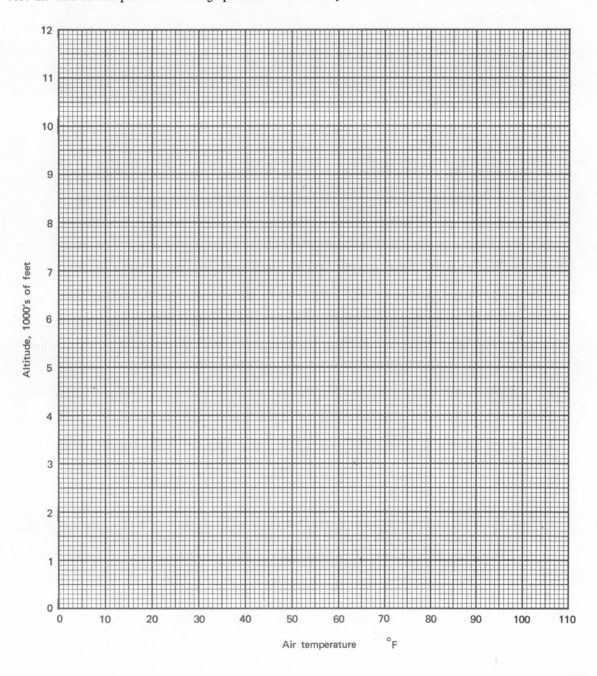

Altitude, 1000's of feet

Air temperature   °F

J4

Exercise J-4 ADIABATIC WARMING AND RAIN SHADOW

Air at temperature of 84°F at sea level rises up over the slopes of a coastal mountain range. By adiabatic cooling the air reaches a dew-point temperature of 51°F. The air continues to rise, at the wet adiabatic rate of 3.2F° per 1000 ft, until, at the mountain summit, temperature has dropped to 35°. The air then descends the lee side of the range, reaching the floor of an interior basin at 1000 ft elevation.

Plot the data on the graph on the reverse side of the page. Label fully. Using the graph as a direct source of information, answer the following questions:

(a) At what elevation was dew-point temperature reached?

Ans. _____ ft

(b) Determine the initial dew-point temperature at sea level.

Ans. _____ °F

(c) Give the elevation of the summit of the mountain range.

Ans. _____ ft

(d) What was the air temperature on arrival at the floor of the interior basin?

Ans. _____ °F

(e) Compare qualitatively the relative humidity of the air at the start and finish of this series of changes.

_____

_____

_____

_____

_____

_____

(f) Suppose the same air was next forced to pass over another mountain range of the same summit elevation farther inland. Would the same series of changes take place again? Explain.

_____

_____

_____

_____

_____

_____

_____

_____

Exercise J-5 THUNDERSTORM RAINFALL

During a short thunderstorm at Hays, Kansas, in early August, rainfall was recorded for each 5-minute period. The table below gives rainfall data in terms of *intensity*, in inches per hour, for each 5-minute period. Plot the intensity data as a bar-graph on page 107, using the left-hand scale.

Calculate the amount (depth, inches) that fell in each 5-minute period. (Divide intensity by 12.) Enter in the second column. In the third column, cumulate the depths and plot as a step graph, using the depth scale on the right-hand side of the graph. The final entry will be the total depth of rainfall during the storm.

Period	Intensity in./hr	Depth, in.	Cumulated Depth, in.
5:05 — 5:10	0.0	0.000	0.000
5:10 — 5:15	2.8	0.233	0.233
5:15 — 5:20	4.8	0.400	0.633
5:20 — 5:25	4.6		
5:25 — 5:30	2.3		
5:30 — 5:35	2.8		
5:35 — 5:40	1.1		
5:40 — 5:45	0.2		
5:45 — 5:50	0.2		
5:50 — 5:55	0.0		

Exercise J-5 *(continued; see page 105 for data)*

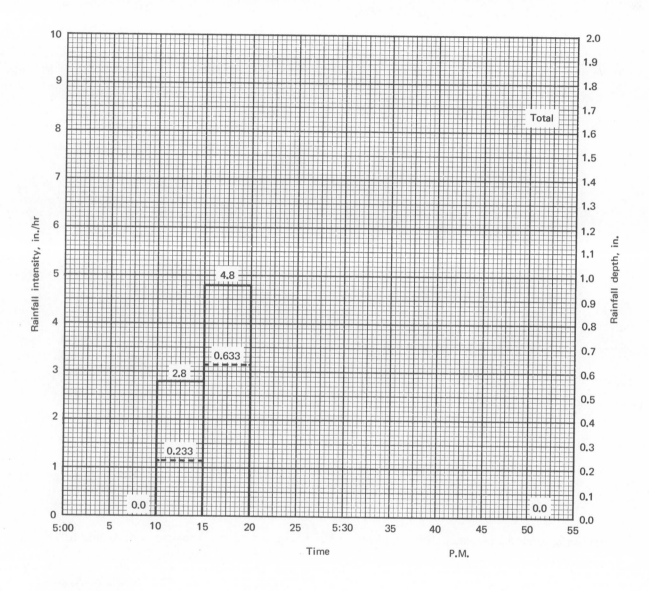

QUESTIONS

(a) What was the total duration of the storm?

Ans. _____ min

(b) What was the greatest depth of fall in any one 10-minute period?

Ans. _____ in.

J6
Exercise J-6 ISOHYETAL MAP

The accompanying map of the lower Ohio Valley region shows the total rainfall during a 4-day rain storm in October. Isohyets have been drawn over a portion of the map. Complete the drawing of the isohyets. Label the 5- and 10-inch lines. (Data of D. W. Mead.)

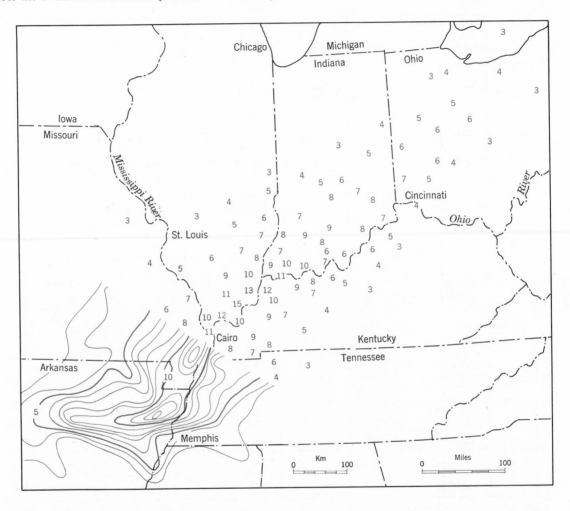

Explain in detail the procedure to be followed in order to calculate the total volume of water that fell during the storm. (Data are necessarily limited to areas with more than 3 inches depth.)

_____

_____

_____

_____

_____

_____

_____

_____

108

Group K

CYCLONIC STORMS, AIR MASSES, AND FRONTS

Text References

Strahler, 1969, *Physical Geography, 3rd Edition*, Chapter 12, pp. 199–215.
Strahler, 1970, *Introduction to Physical Geography, 2nd Edition*, Chapter 7, pp. 106–119.

Map to accompany Exercise K-3.

A daily weather map of the world for a given day during July or August might look like this map which is a composite of typical weather conditions. (After M. A. Garbell.)

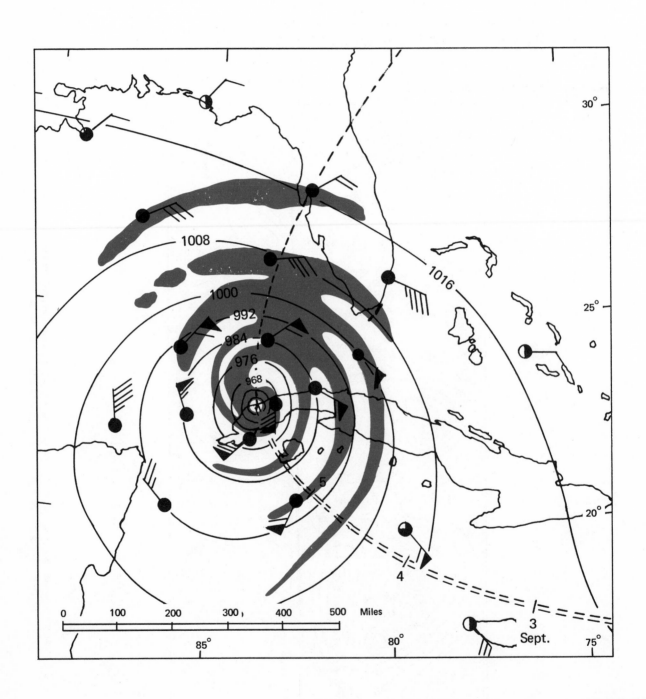

Exercise K-1 INTERPRETATION OF WEATHER MAPS

Weather maps on pages 113 and 115 show changes in position and form of a cyclonic storm on successive days. Remove the two pages and place them side by side for comparison.

(a) Profiles Along Line of Storm Track (Profiles 1-A and 1-B)

Cut out the upper profile graph sheet on page 117 and fix it with tape to the profile line 1-A on Map A. Construct a pressure profile across the map. Several points have been plotted and a partial profile drawn, illustrating the procedure to be followed.

  Mark high pressure crests with the letter "H," low troughs with "L." Label the profile fully. Next, remove the profile graph sheet from Map A and transfer it to the corresponding position on Map B. Again construct a pressure profile across the map. Label fully. The completed profile should be removed and pasted into the designated space on p. 112.

QUESTIONS

What distance has the center of low pressure traveled in the 24-hour period? Use the scale of miles on Map B. Give speed in both statute miles per hour and knots.

_____ stat. mi _____ naut. mi

_____ mph _____ knots

By how many millibars has pressure decreased at the cyclone center during the 24-hour period?

  Pressure on Map A _____ mb

  Pressure on Map B _____ mb   Difference _____ mb

(b) Profiles Across Cold Front (Profiles 2-A and 2-B)

Follow the same procedure as in (a), above. Construct profiles across the maps along lines 2-A and 2-B. Label as above. Mark location of the cold front on each profile.

QUESTIONS

What distance has the cold front traveled in the 24-hour period? Give the speed in both statute miles per hour and knots.

_____ stat. mi _____ naut. mi

_____ mph _____ knots

By what amount has pressure in the cold front trough changed in the 24-hour period?

  Pressure on Map A _____ mb   Direction of change _____

  Pressure on Map B _____ mb   Difference _____ mb

K₁

Space for Completed Profiles for Exercise K-1

(Place profiles 1-A, 1-B here)

(Place profiles 2-A, 2-B here)

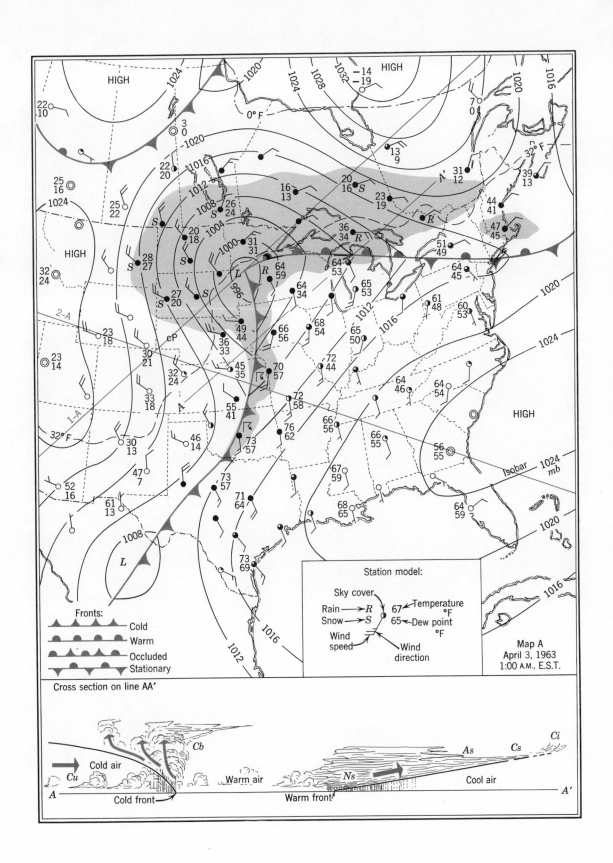

Fronts:
- Cold
- Warm
- Occluded
- Stationary

Station model:

Sky cover

Rain → R

Snow → S

Wind speed

Wind direction

67 ← Temperature °F

65 ← Dew point °F

Map A
April 3, 1963
1:00 A.M., E.S.T.

Cross section on line AA'

Cold air

Cu

Cb

Cold front

Warm air

Ns

Warm front

Cool air

As

Cs

Ci

A

A'

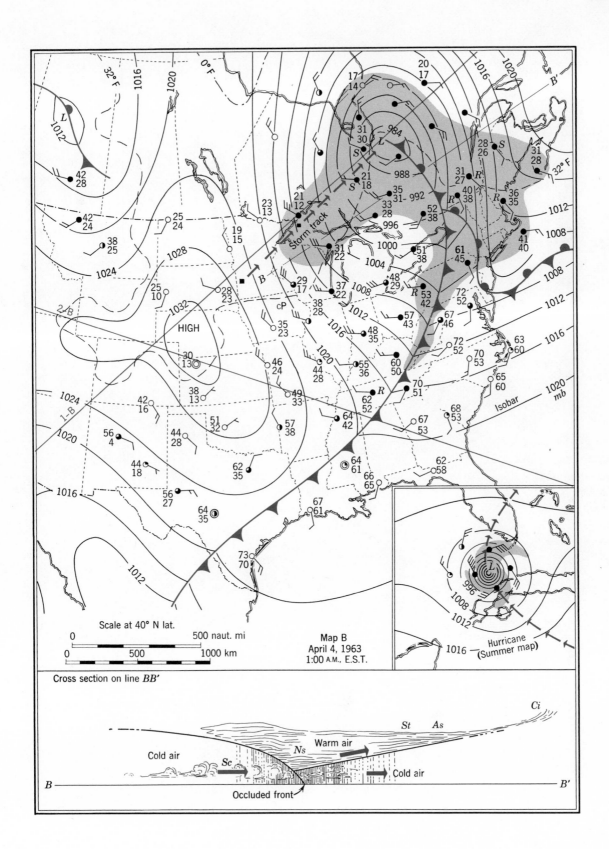

Scale at 40° N lat.

0   500 naut. mi

0   500   1000 km

Map B
April 4, 1963
1:00 A.M., E.S.T.

Hurricane
(Summer map)

Cross section on line BB'

Ci

St   As

Cold air   Sc   Ns   Warm air

Cold air

B   B'

Occluded front

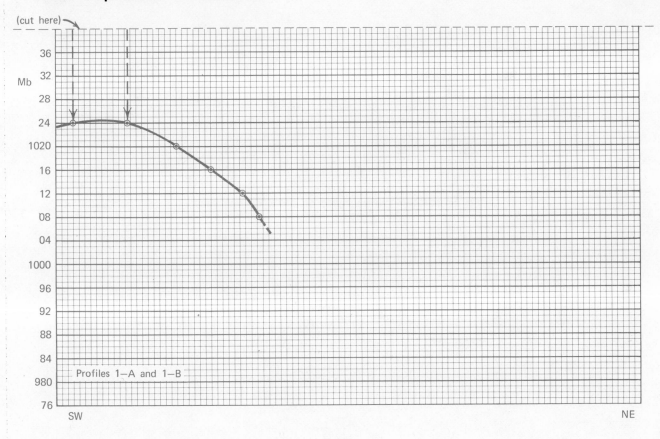

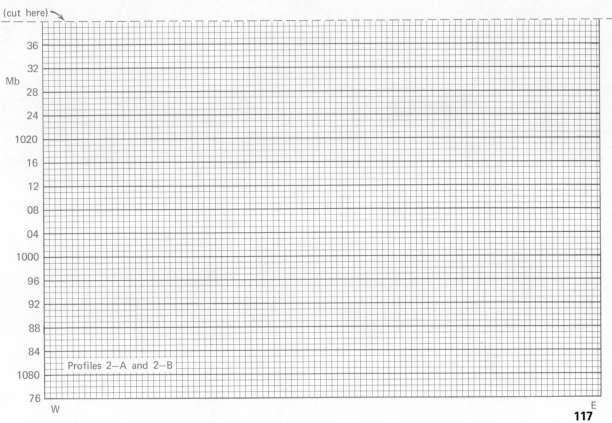

Profile Graph Sheets for Exercise K-1.

K_1

117

Exercise K-1 *(continued)*

(c) Temperature Changes

On each weather map (pages 113 and 115) draw the 60° isotherm of air temperature. Compare the positions of these isotherms on successive days.

Explain how the form and location of the 60° isotherm is related to fronts and air masses.

_____

_____

_____

_____

On Map A, note temperatures in the high pressure center over Hudson Bay. Compare with temperatures in the high over Georgia. Explain the great difference in temperatures in these two highs.

_____

_____

_____

_____

(d) Winds

Compare wind directions in southwestern Missouri on Maps A and B. What change of direction has taken place? What term is applied to such a change? What is the cause of the change?

_____

_____

_____

_____

Compare wind directions along the western shore of Lake Superior on Maps A and B. Answer the same questions as above.

_____

_____

_____

_____

_____

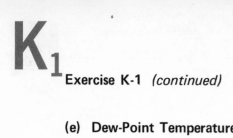

(e) Dew-Point Temperatures

Study the dew-point temperatures in relation to corresponding air temperatures at various stations on Map A, particularly in the vicinity of the cyclone and on either side of the cold front and warm front.

Where is the dew-point temperature equal to the air temperature? What is the significance of this equality?

_____

_____

_____

_____

What is the significance of the relatively high dew-point temperatures in the area east of the cold front and south of the warm front?

_____

_____

_____

_____

What is the significance of the large difference between dew-point temperature and air temperature in south-eastern New Mexico?

_____

_____

_____

_____

(f) Air Masses

Based on the above study of dew-point temperatures and air temperatures, identify the various air masses present. Label these air masses by means of conventional symbols on both maps.

(g) Clouds and Precipitation

What type of cloud and precipitation are indicated along the cold front in Kansas and Oklahoma on Map A?

_____

What type of cloud and precipitation are found in northern Minnesota on Map A?

_____

On Map A, where are stations showing calm with clear sky located? Explain this distribution.

_____

_____

_____

Exercise K-2 TROPICAL CYCLONE

Examine the hurricane shown on the inset area on Map B, page 115. Note its small diameter in comparison with the cyclonic storm shown on the main part of the map. Note the steep barometric gradient and strong winds, forming a counterclockwise in-spiral.

Refer to the map on page 110, showing a similar hurricane. It is a mature tropical storm of large size and severe intensity, centered over western Cuba at 1:00 A.M. on September 6. The storm track shows positions of the center on preceding dates. Precipitation patern is interpreted from radar observations.

Graph of Hurricane Passage

The blank graph below is organized to show meteorological elements at an observing station in the path of the storm. Let it be assumed that the storm follows a track as shown by the dashed line, passing over Tampa, Florida. The speed of the storm is assumed constant, requiring exactly two days to bring the eye of the hurricane over Tampa at 1:00 A.M. September 8.

On a sheet of tracing paper, trace off the isobars and wind arrows from the map. Divide the storm track into segments representing 8-hour time intervals. Move the tracing paper successively from one 8-hour position to the next. Estimate the barometric pressure, wind speed, and wind direction at Tampa at each position. Plot these data on the graph, using the vertical scales provided. Draw a wind arrow above each plotted point to show direction. Extend the observations to show meteorological conditions through September 9.

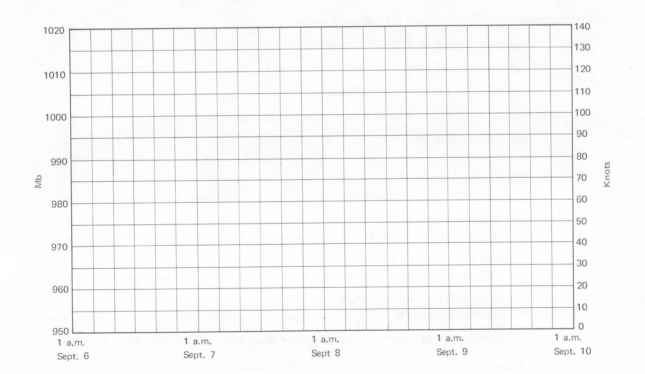

K2, 3

Exercise K-2 QUESTIONS

(a) What was the barometric pressure in the eye of the hurricane?

_____ mb

(b) At Tampa, as the storm approached, was the rate of pressure fall more rapid or less rapid than the pressure rise as the storm moved away?

_____

(c) Estimate the highest wind speed observed.

_____ knots

(d) What conditions of wind speed existed in the eye of the storm?

_____

_____

Exercise J-3 WORLD WEATHER ON A DAY IN SUMMER

Refer to the world map on page 109 and answer the following questions:

(a) How many low-pressure centers are shown on this map?

_____

(b) How many high-pressure centers are shown?

_____

(c) How many lows fall into each of the following classes?

    (1) Extratropical (middle-latitude) cyclones: _____

    (2) Tropical cyclones: _____

    (3) Weak lows of the equatorial trough: _____

(d) At what approximate latitude, or latitude belt, is each of the following located?

    (1) Equatorial trough: _____

    (2) Subtropical cells of high pressure, northern hemisphere: _____

    (3) Subtropical cells of high pressure, southern hemisphere: _____

    (4) Middle-latitude cyclone centers, northern hemisphere: _____

    (5) Middle-latitude cyclone centers, southern hemisphere: _____

(e) Of the middle latitude cyclones shown on this map, how many are occluded, how many are open?

    Occluded _____   Open _____

Group L

CLIMATE CLASSIFICATION AND CLIMATIC REGIMES

L

Text References

Strahler, 1969, *Physical Geography, 3rd Edition*, Chapter 13, pp. 219–236.
Strahler, 1970, *Introduction to Physical Geography, 2nd Edition*, Chapter 8, pp. 121–135.

Climate Data for Exercise L-1

(Data from Austin and Haurwitz, *Climatology*.)

		J	F	M	A	M	J	J	A	S	O	N	D	Year
(a)	°F	13.3	13.6	27.0	43.9	53.8	62.2	69.1	65.8	56.1	43.9	30.9	20.1	41.5
	In.	0.7	0.6	0.5	1.0	2.0	2.9	1.8	1.2	1.3	0.7	0.6	0.6	13.9
(b)	°F	−14.4	7.4	13.3	33.8	46.8	58.5	62.6	58.5	46.0	30.0	6.8	−9.2	27.1
	In.	0.1	0.1	0.1	0.4	0.9	1.7	2.4	3.0	1.3	0.3	0.2	0.2	10.3
(c)	°F	71.1	73.6	83.1	91.6	94.5	93.7	89.2	86.5	89.2	88.9	80.8	71.1	84.4
	In.	0	0	0.1	0	0.3	0.9	3.5	2.8	1.1	0.4	0	0	9.0
(d)	°F	33.4	35.2	41.9	53.2	64.0	72.1	76.6	75.0	68.0	57.7	46.2	36.9	55.0
	In.	3.4	3.7	3.6	3.4	3.5	3.9	4.6	4.3	3.4	2.8	2.6	3.3	42.5
(e)	°F	47.8	49.5	52.5	58.3	66.4	74.1	79.7	79.5	73.2	66.2	57.0	57.8	63.0
	In.	2.2	1.8	1.3	0.9	0.8	0.6	0.3	0.6	0.7	1.4	2.9	2.5	16.0
(f)	°F	77.9	78.4	79.3	79.9	80.6	79.9	80.2	79.7	79.5	79.7	79.0	78.3	79.3
	In.	9.7	7.1	7.3	7.8	6.5	7.0	6.7	7.8	6.9	7.9	10.1	10.5	95.1
(g)	°F	80.8	80.6	80.8	80.4	78.4	75.0	74.8	78.1	81.3	82.6	81.7	81.0	79.7
	In.	9.6	8.9	8.1	4.1	2.0	0.2	0.1	1.1	2.0	4.4	6.0	7.9	54.5
(h)	°F	−14.3	−12.8	−2.0	12.0	28.6	38.7	45.7	44.2	36.3	26.1	12.4	−3.8	17.6
	In.	1.1	1.3	0.8	1.5	1.5	1.1	2.6	2.0	1.2	1.5	2.2	1.5	18.3
(i)	°F	63.3	63.0	62.2	58.3	54.1	51.6	50.4	53.4	60.1	63.5	64.6	63.9	59.0
	In.	10.6	8.4	8.3	2.2	0.9	0.6	0.8	0.3	0.3	1.3	3.5	8.5	45.7
(j)	°F	22.6	23.9	31.6	42.4	52.5	61.9	67.5	65.7	59.2	49.6	37.9	27.7	45.1
	In.	3.9	4.3	3.8	3.4	3.3	3.3	3.2	3.1	3.1	3.1	3.5	3.9	41.9

KÖPPEN-GEIGER SYSTEM OF CLIMATE CLASSIFICATION
After R. Geiger and W. Pohl (1953)

Key to letter code designating climate regions:

FIRST LETTER

A, C, D Sufficient heat and precipitation for growth of high-trunked trees.

A *Tropical climates*. All monthly mean temperatures over 64.4°F (18°C).

B *Dry climates*. Boundaries determined by formula using mean annual temperature and mean annual precipitation (see graphs).

C *Warm temperate climates*. Mean temperature of coldest month: 64.4°F (18°C) down to 26.6°F (−3°C).

D *Snow climates*. Warmest month mean over 50°F (10°C). Coldest month mean under 26.6°F (−3°C).

E *Ice climates*. Warmest month mean under 50°F (10°C).

SECOND LETTER

S Steppe climate. }
W Desert climate. }   — Boundaries determined by formulas (See graphs).

f Sufficient precipitation in all months.
m Rainforest despite a dry season (i.e., monsoon cycle).
s Dry season in summer of the respective hemisphere.
w Dry season in winter of the respective hemisphere.

THIRD LETTER

a Warmest month mean over 71.6°F (22°C).
b Warmest month mean under 71.6°F (22°C). At least 4 months have means over 50°F (10°C.)
c Fewer than 4 months with means over 50°F (10°C).
d Same as c, but coldest month mean under −36.4°F (−38°C).
h Dry and hot. Mean annual temperature over 64.4°F (18°C).
k Dry and cold. Mean annual temperature under 64.4°F (18°C).

BOUNDARIES OF DRY CLIMATES

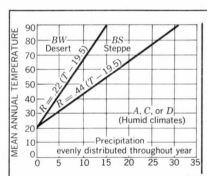
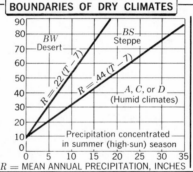
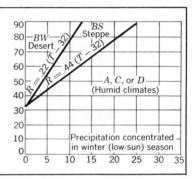

R = MEAN ANNUAL PRECIPITATION, INCHES

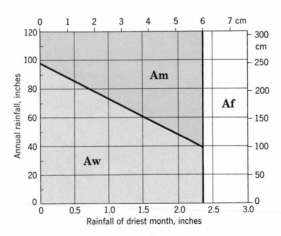

This graph shows how *Aw* climates are distinguished
from *Am* climates in the Köppen system.
(After Haurwitz and Austin.)

Exercise L-1 IDENTIFICATION OF KÖPPEN CLIMATES

Refer to page 123 for climate data of 10 stations, designated by letters (a) through (j). Monthly mean temperatures (°F) and annual mean temperature are given in the upper line of figures. The lower line gives mean monthly precipitation in inches, and mean annual total.

Determine the Köppen climate group to which each station belongs. Give the first two letters of the Köppen code. If possible, determine the third letter as well. Refer to the Köppen system key on page 124.

In each case, state the criteria used in assigning the station to the Köppen climate.

(a) Code _____ Criteria _____
_____
_____
_____

(b) Code _____ Criteria _____
_____
_____
_____

(c) Code _____ Criteria _____
_____
_____
_____

(d) Code _____ Criteria _____
_____
_____
_____

(e) Code _____ Criteria _____
_____
_____
_____

(f) Code _____ Criteria _____
_____
_____
_____

(g) Code _____ Criteria _____
_____
_____
_____

(h) Code _____   Criteria _____

_____

_____

_____

(i) Code _____   Criteria _____

_____

_____

_____

(j) Code _____   Criteria _____

_____

_____

_____

Use this space for additional explanation.

Exercise L-2 CLIMATIC REGIMES

On the reverse side of this page is a table of temperature and precipitation data for 10 stations, each exhibiting the characteristics of one of the climatic regimes, or a combination of regimes.

Plot the monthly data of each station on a thermohyet diagram plotting chart, pages 129, 130, and 131. Plot one point for each month, then connect the points with straight lines. Label each point with the initial of the month. Place arrows to show the direction of the annual cycle. Label with name of station.

Using the blank spaces on pages 133 and 134, write a brief statement for each station, explaining how the annual cycle of temperature and precipitation exemplifies the salient features of the climatic regime to which it has been assigned. Include mention of the seasonal properties of the climate as shown in the closed loop of the annual cycle.

List of stations	*Köppen Code*
(a) Stanley, Falkland Islands	EM
(b) Madang, New Guinea	Af
(c) Cochin, India	Am
(d) Port Darwin, N. T., Australia	Aw
(e) Sacramento, California, U. S. A.	Csa
(f) Winnipeg, Manitoba, Canada	Dfb
(g) Lima, Peru	BWh
(h) Port Nolloth, Union of South Africa	BWk
(i) Kazalinsk, Kazak, U. S. S. R.	BWk
(j) Dawson, Yukon Territory, Canada	Dfc

CLIMATE DATA FOR EXERCISE L-2

		J	F	M	A	M	J	J	A	S	O	N	D	Year
(a) Stanley, Falkland Is. 51° 42'S, 57° 51'W, 6 ft	°F	49	48	46.5	43	39	36	35.5	36	39	41.5	44.5	46.5	42
	In	2.8	2.3	2.5	2.6	2.6	2.1	2.0	2.0	1.5	1.6	2.0	2.8	26.8
(b) Madang, New Guinea 05° 14'S, 145° 45'E, 20 ft	°F	81	80.5	80.5	81	81.5	81	81	81	81	81.5	81.5	81.5	81
	In	12.1	11.9	14.9	16.9	15.1	10.8	7.6	4.8	5.3	10.0	13.3	14.5	137.2
(c) Cochin, India 09° 58'N, 76° 14'E, 10 ft	°F	80.5	82	84	85.5	84	80	79	79.5	80	80	81.5	81	81.5
	In	0.9	0.8	2.0	4.9	11.7	28.5	23.3	13.9	7.7	13.4	6.7	1.6	115.3
(d) Port Darwin, Northern Territory, Australia 12° 28'S, 130° 51'E, 97 ft	°F	83.5	83.5	84	84	82	78.5	77	79.5	87.5	85	86	85	82.5
	In	15.2	12.3	10.0	3.8	0.6	0.1	<0.1	0.1	0.5	2.0	4.7	9.4	58.7
(e) Sacramento, California, U. S. A. 38° 35'N, 121° 30'W, 69 ft	°F	45.5	50.5	55	58.5	64	70	74	73	70	62.5	54	46.5	60.5
	In	3.8	2.8	2.8	1.5	0.8	0.1	<0.1	<0.1	0.3	0.8	1.9	3.8	18.6
(f) Winnipeg, Manitoba, Canada 49° 54'N, 97° 14'W, 786 ft	°F	−3	0.5	16	37.5	52	62	67	63.5	54	41	21.5	6	35.5
	In	0.9	0.9	1.2	1.4	2.3	3.1	3.1	2.5	2.3	1.5	1.1	0.9	21.2
(g) Lima, Peru 12° 05'S, 77° 03'W, 394 ft	°F	74	75	74.5	76.5	67	63	62	61	62.5	64.5	67	70	68
	In	0.1	<0.1	<0.1	<0.1	0.2	0.2	0.3	0.3	0.3	0.1	0.1	<0.1	1.6
(h) Port Nolloth, Union of South Africa 29° 14'S, 16° 52'E, 23 ft	°F	60	60.5	60	58	57	55.5	53.5	54	55	56.5	58.5	59.5	57
	In	0.1	0.1	0.2	0.2	0.3	0.3	0.3	0.3	0.2	0.1	0.1	0.1	2.3
(i) Kazalinsk, Kazak, U. S. S. R. 45° 46'N, 62° 06'E, 207 ft	°F	10.5	13	26	42.5	64	73.5	77.5	73	61.5	46	30	19.5	45
	In	0.4	0.4	0.5	0.5	0.6	0.2	0.2	0.3	0.3	0.4	0.5	0.6	4.9
(j) Dawson, Yukon Territory, Canada 64° 04'N, 139° 29'W, 1062 ft	°F	−21	−12	4	28.5	46.5	56.5	59.5	54.5	42	26	1.5	−14	23
	In	0.9	0.7	0.5	0.5	1.0	1.2	1.5	1.5	1.4	1.2	1.1	1.0	12.6

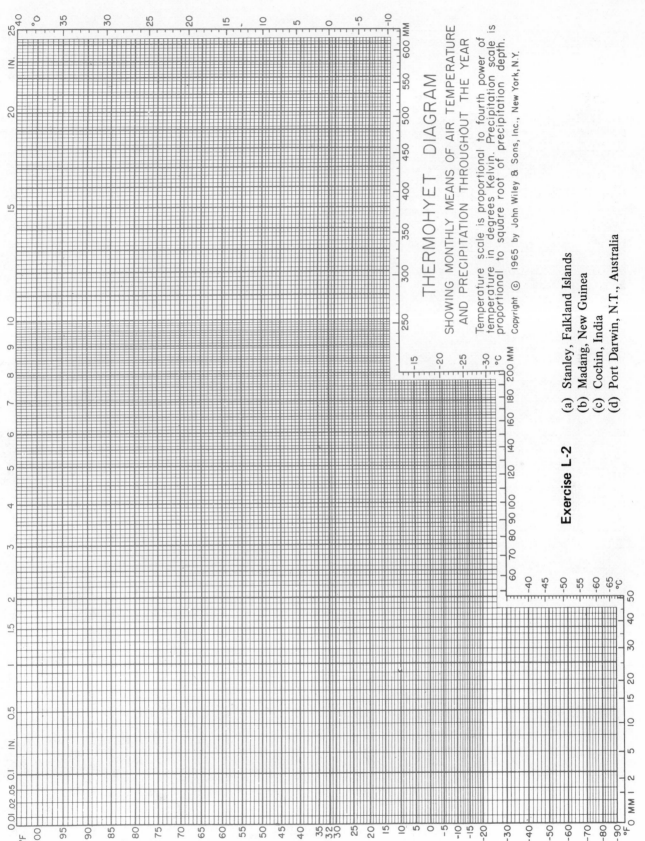

THERMOHYET DIAGRAM

SHOWING MONTHLY MEANS OF AIR TEMPERATURE
AND PRECIPITATION THROUGHOUT THE YEAR

Temperature scale is proportional to fourth power of
temperature in degrees Kelvin. Precipitation scale is
proportional to square root of precipitation depth.

Copyright © 1965 by John Wiley & Sons, Inc., New York, N.Y.

Exercise L-2

(a) Stanley, Falkland Islands
(b) Madang, New Guinea
(c) Cochin, India
(d) Port Darwin, N.T., Australia

L₂

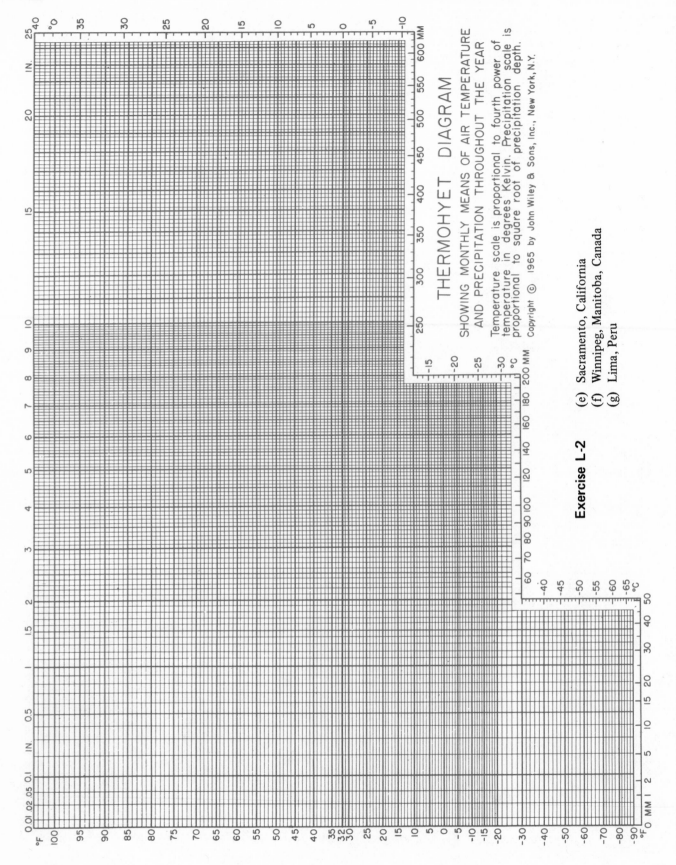

THERMOHYET DIAGRAM

SHOWING MONTHLY MEANS OF AIR TEMPERATURE
AND PRECIPITATION THROUGHOUT THE YEAR

Temperature scale is proportional to fourth power of
temperature in degrees Kelvin. Precipitation scale is
proportional to square root of precipitation depth.

Copyright © 1965 by John Wiley & Sons, Inc., New York, N.Y.

Exercise L-2   (e) Sacramento, California
(f) Winnipeg, Manitoba, Canada
(g) Lima, Peru

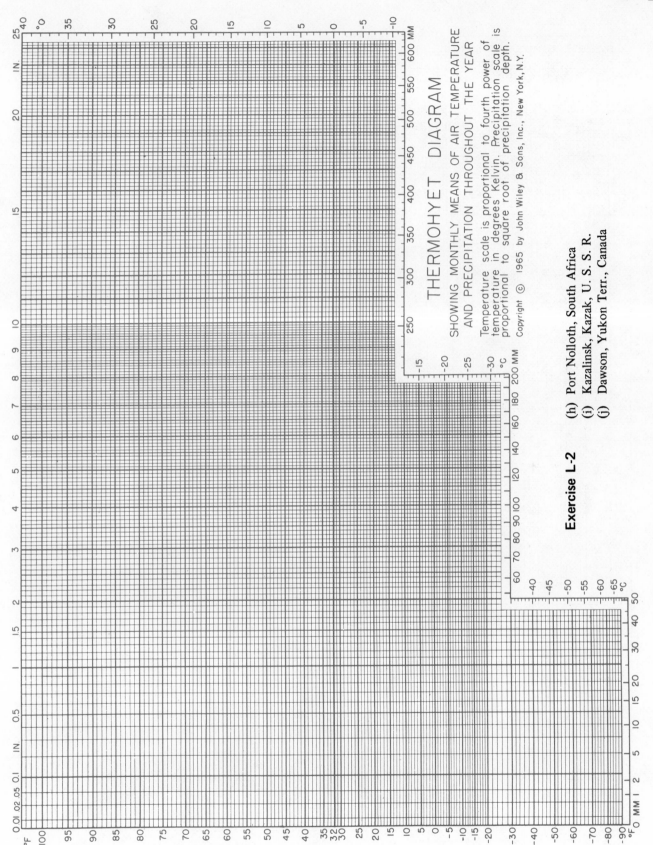

THERMOHYET DIAGRAM

SHOWING MONTHLY MEANS OF AIR TEMPERATURE
AND PRECIPITATION THROUGHOUT THE YEAR

Temperature scale is proportional to fourth power of
temperature in degrees Kelvin. Precipitation scale is
proportional to square root of precipitation depth.

Copyright © 1965 by John Wiley & Sons, Inc., New York, N.Y.

Exercise L-2

(h) Port Nolloth, South Africa
(i) Kazalinsk, Kazak, U. S. S. R.
(j) Dawson, Yukon Terr., Canada

L₂ Extra Thermohyet Diagram Plotting Chart to Accompany Exercise L-2

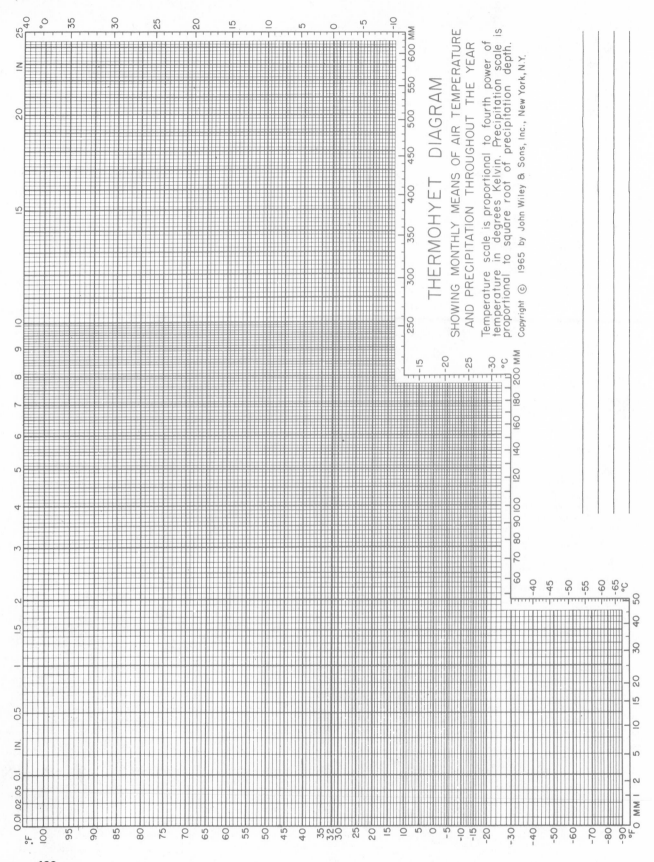

THERMOHYET DIAGRAM

SHOWING MONTHLY MEANS OF AIR TEMPERATURE
AND PRECIPITATION THROUGHOUT THE YEAR

Temperature scale is proportional to fourth power of
temperature in degrees Kelvin. Precipitation scale is
proportional to square root of precipitation depth.

Copyright © 1965 by John Wiley & Sons, Inc., New York, N.Y.

Exercise L-2 (See instructions on page 127)

(a) Stanley, Falkland Islands. Middle-latitude equable regime.

_____

_____

_____

_____

_____

(b) Madang, New Guinea. Equatorial regime.

_____

_____

_____

_____

(c) Cochin, India. Equatorial regime with strong monsoon effect.

_____

_____

_____

_____

_____

(d) Port Darwin, N.T., Australia. Tropical wet-dry regime.

_____

_____

_____

_____

(e) Sacramento, California. Mediterranean regime.

_____

_____

_____

_____

_____

Exercise L-2 *(continued)*

(f) Winnipeg, Manitoba, Canada. Continental regime.

_____

_____

_____

_____

_____

(g) Lima, Peru. Desert regime.

_____

_____

_____

_____

(h) Port Nolloth, Union of South Africa. Desert regime with Mediterranean tendency.

_____

_____

_____

_____

_____

(i) Kazalinsk, Kazak, U. S. S. R. Desert regime combined with continental regime.

_____

_____

_____

_____

(j) Dawson, Yukon Terr., Canada. Polar regime combined with continental regime.

_____

_____

_____

_____

_____

Group M

THE WATER BUDGET

Text References

Strahler, 1969, *Physical Geography, 3rd Edition*, Chapter 14, pp. 237–250.
Strahler, 1970, *Introduction to Physical Geography, 2nd Edition*, Chapter 9, pp. 143–146.

General Instructions

The tables below give monthly mean precipitation (cm) and monthly mean evapotranspiration (cm) for three stations. Plot these data on the graphs on pages 137, 139, and 141. Follow the example given on p. 136 for Seattle, Washington. A step-graph is used, instead of a smooth curve, because the quantities involved are monthly totals.

Use two colors in plotting the data. For example, use black for precipitation; red for evapotranspiration. Enter the monthly quantity above each step in the graph, as this will facilitate budget analysis. Determine areas of water surplus, water deficiency, soil-moisture utilization (10 cm), and recharge (10 cm). Label these areas and color them with pencil or crayon to set each apart from the others. Calculate the total quantities of water surplus and deficiency and enter these values on the graph.

(a) Seabrook, New Jersey.

(Köppen, Cfa) (Data from C. W. Thornthwaite and J. R. Mather, 1955)

	J	F	M	A	M	J	J	A	S	O	N	D	Year
Precipitation (cm)	8.7	9.3	10.2	8.8	9.2	9.1	11.2	11.3	8.2	8.5	7.0	9.3	110.8
Pot. E-T (cm)	0.1	0.2	1.6	4.6	9.2	13.1	15.4	13.6	9.7	5.3	1.9	0.3	75.0

(b) Berkeley, California.

(Köppen, Csb) (Data from C. W. Thornthwaite and J. R. Mather, 1955)

	J	F	M	A	M	J	J	A	S	O	N	D	Year
Precipitation (cm)	13.0	11.2	9.4	3.7	2.4	0.5	0.1	0.1	1.3	3.1	6.2	10.6	61.6
Pot. E-T (cm)	2.6	3.2	4.5	5.6	7.1	8.4	8.8	8.2	7.5	6.3	4.3	2.8	69.3

(c) Kayes, Mali.

(Köppen, BSh) (Data from D. B. Carter, 1954)

	J	F	M	A	M	J	J	A	S	O	N	D	Year
Precipitation (cm)	0	0	0.1	0.3	1.7	9.5	18.4	21.4	14.0	4.0	0.1	0.2	69.7
Pot. E-T (cm)	9.6	13.0	17.4	18.9	20.2	18.8	17.1	15.8	15.6	16.4	14.8	9.3	186.9

M

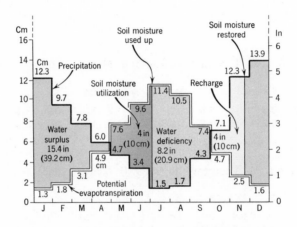

Water budget of Seattle, Washington.
(After C. W. Thornthwaite, *The Geographical Review,* **1948.)**

M₁

Exercise M-1 WATER BUDGET OF SEABROOK, N. J.

Refer to general instructions on page 135.

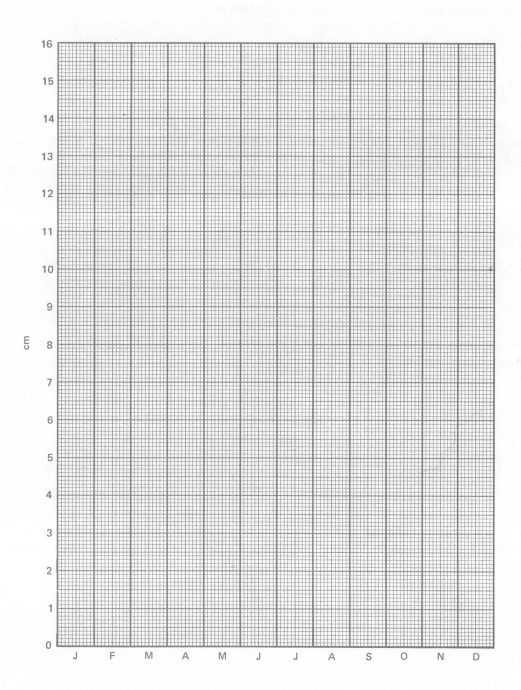

(Answer questions on reverse side of page.)

M₁
QUESTIONS

(a) In what months does precipitation exceed or equal potential evapotranspiration?

_____

_____

In what months does potential evapotranspiration exceed precipitation?

_____

_____

(b) Does the total water deficiency exceed the soil moisture utilization at Seabrook?

_____

Would irrigation be either desirable or essential for crop farming in this climate? If so, when would it be needed?

_____

_____

_____

_____

_____

(c) What climatic regime prevails in the area of Seabrook, N. J.? How does the water budget reflect this regime?

_____

_____

_____

_____

_____

(d) Construct a scale of inches for the graph. Mark and label this scale along the right-hand edge of the graph.

Exercise M-2 WATER BUDGET OF BERKELEY, CALIFORNIA

Refer to general instructions on page 135.

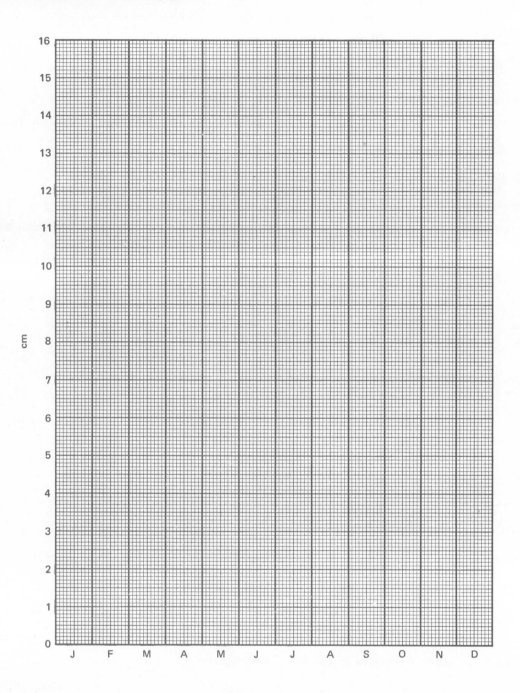

QUESTIONS

(a) In how many months of the year does precipitation exceed potential evapotranspiration? Name the months.

_____

_____ 139

(b) In how many months of the year does potential evapotranspiration exceed precipitation. Name the months.

_____

_____

Compare this yearly pattern with that of Seabrook. What is the outstanding point of contrast?

_____

_____

_____

_____

(c) Which station has the larger water deficiency, Berkeley or Seabrook? Give the amounts.

_____

(d) Explain why Berkeley has substantial monthly amounts of potential evapotranspiration throughout the winter months (December through February) whereas Seabrook has almost none.

_____

_____

_____

_____

(e) What is the outstanding difference in the annual precipitation cycles of Berkeley and Seabrook? How does this difference influence the annual water budget?

_____

_____

_____

_____

(f) Explain the necessity for extensive summer crop irrigation in a climate such as that of Berkeley.

_____

_____

_____

_____

(g) What climatic regime is represented by the data of Berkeley?

_____

_____

(h) Add a scale in inches to the right-hand side of the graph.

Exercise M-3 WATER BUDGET OF KAYES, MALI

Refer to general instructions on page 135.

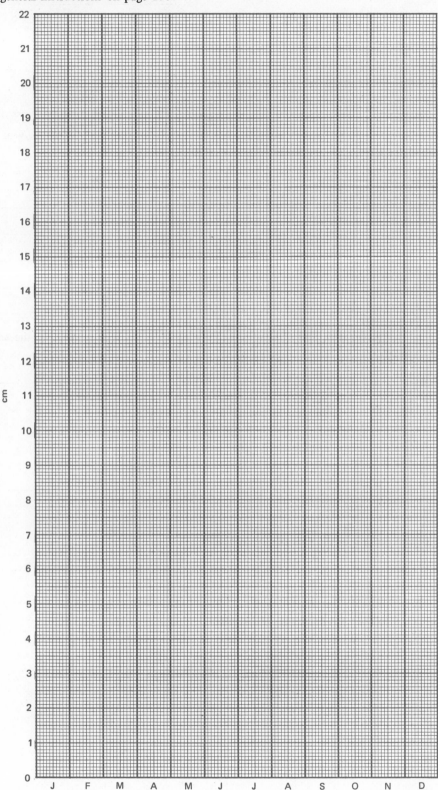

M3

QUESTIONS

(a) Does any water surplus occur in the annual water budget of Kayes?

_____

How much is the amount of recharge?

_____

Does recharge exceed the assumed soil moisture capacity of 10 cm?

_____

(b) Explain why the potential evapotranspiration graph has two peaks, or maxima, during the year. (Consider the nature of the annual air temperature cycle at this location.)

_____

_____

_____

_____

_____

_____

(c) Compare the graph for Kayes with that of Seabrook (Exercise M-1). In what respect do the annual patterns differ strikingly?

_____

_____

_____

_____

_____

_____

(d) What climatic regime prevails in the area of Kayes, Mali?

_____

_____

(e) Add a scale of inches to the right-hand side of the graph.

Group N

EQUATORIAL AND TROPICAL CLIMATES

Text References

Strahler, 1969, *Physical Geography, 3rd Edition,* Chapter 15, pp. 251–266.
Strahler, 1970, *Introduction to Physical Geography, 2nd Edition,* Chapter 10, pp. 149–160.

General Instructions

Blank climographs on following pages are to be used for plotting climate data for stations given on the reverse side of this page.

Mean monthly temperatures (°F) are to be plotted as points centered in each monthly column. The points are then connected by line segments, or by a smooth curve, showing the annual temperature cycle.

Mean monthly precipitation totals (in inches) are plotted as horizontal lines extending across the month, and are joined into a step-graph.

After the data have been plotted, calculate the following values:

(1) Mean annual temperature. (Sum of monthly means divided by 12.)

(2) Mean annual temperature range. (Difference between highest and lowest monthly means.)

(3) Mean annual total precipitation. (Sum of monthly values.)

Enter the above values in the blank spaces beside each climograph.

Blank thermohyet diagrams are also provided on following pages. Plot the data of each station, as was done in Exercise L-2, page 127. Label fully. Use different colored pencils, if desired, to distinguish stations having an overlap of figures.

CLIMATE DATA (From Trewartha and Meteorological Office of Great Britain.)

Exercise N-1 BELÉM, BRAZIL, 1°S

	J	F	M	A	M	J	J	A	S	O	N	D
Temperature, °F	77.7	77.0	77.5	77.7	78.4	78.3	78.1	78.3	78.6	79.0	79.7	79.0
Precipitation, in.	11.6	12.9	14.9	12.1	9.4	6.7	6.2	4.5	3.5	2.8	2.6	6.0

Exercise N-2 CAIRO, EGYPT, U. A. R. 30°N

	J	F	M	A	M	J	J	A	S	O	N	D
Temperature, °F	56	58.5	63.5	70	77	81.5	83	83	79	75.5	68	59
Precipitation, in.	0.2	0.2	0.2	0.1	0.1	<0.1	0.0	0.0	<0.1	<0.1	0.1	0.2

Exercise N-3 AKYAB, BURMA, 20°N

	J	F	M	A	M	J	J	A	S	O	N	D
Temperature, °F	70	72.5	78	82.5	84	81.5	80.5	80.5	81.5	81.5	78	72
Precipitation, in.	0.1	0.2	0.4	2.0	15.4	45.3	55.1	44.6	22.7	11.3	5.1	0.7

Exercise N-4 CUYABA, BRAZIL, 15½°S

	J	F	M	A	M	J	J	A	S	O	N	D
Temperature, °F	81	81	81	80	78	75	76	78	82	82	82	81
Precipitation, in.	9.8	8.3	8.3	4.0	2.1	0.3	0.2	1.1	2.0	4.5	5.9	8.1

Exercise N-5 BENARES, INDIA, 25°N

	J	F	M	A	M	J	J	A	S	O	N	D
Temperature, °F	60	65	77	87	91	89	84	83	83	78	68	60
Precipitation, in.	0.7	0.6	0.4	0.2	0.6	4.8	12.1	11.6	7.1	2.1	0.2	0.2

Exercise N-6 ANTOFAGASTA, CHILE, 24°S

	J	F	M	A	M	J	J	A	S	O	N	D
Temperature, °F	69.5	69.5	67.5	64	61	58.5	57	57	58.5	60.5	63.5	66
Precipitation, in.	0.0	0.0	0.0	<0.1	<0.1	0.1	0.2	0.1	<0.1	0.1	<0.1	0.0

Exercise N-7 CAIRNS, QUEENSLAND, AUSTRALIA, 17°S

	J	F	M	A	M	J	J	A	S	O	N	D
Temperature, °F	82	81.5	80	77.5	73.5	71.5	69.5	71	73.5	77	79	81.5
Precipitation, in.	16.6	15.7	18.1	11.3	4.4	2.9	1.6	1.7	1.7	2.1	3.9	8.7

CLIMOGRAPHS

Exercise N-1 BELÉM, BRAZIL

Mean Ann. Temp.   _____°F

Mean Ann. Temp. Ra.   _____F°

Mean Ann. Precip.   _____in.

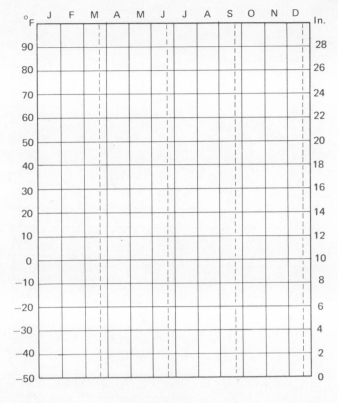

Exercise N-2 CAIRO, U. A. R.

Mean Ann. Temp.   _____°F

Mean Ann. Temp. Ra.   _____F°

Mean Ann. Precip.   _____in.

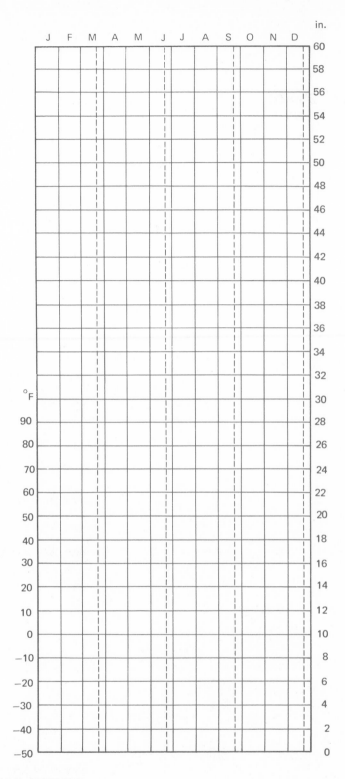

Exercise N-3 AKYAB, BURMA

Mean Ann. Temp. _____ °F

Mean Ann. Temp. Ra. _____ F°

Mean Ann. Precip. _____ in.

Exercise N-4 CUYABA, BRAZIL

Mean Ann. Temp. _____ °F

Mean Ann. Temp. Ra. _____ F°

Mean Ann. Precip. _____ in.

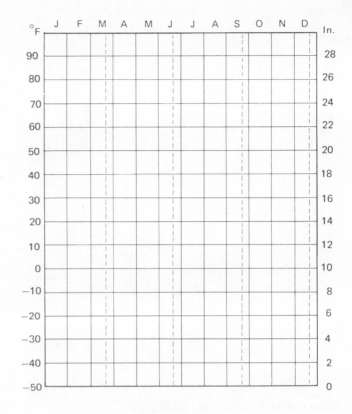

Exercise N-5 BENARES, INDIA

Mean Ann. Temp. _____ °F

Mean Ann. Temp. Ra. _____ F°

Mean Ann. Precip. _____ in.

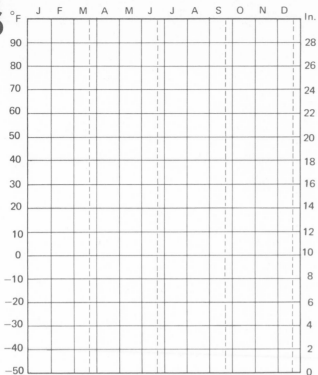

N₆

Exercise N-6 ANTOFAGASTA, CHILE

Mean Ann. Temp.　　————————　°F

Mean Ann. Temp. Ra.　————————　F°

Mean Ann. Precip.　　————————　in.

Exercise N-7 CAIRNS, QUEENS-
LAND, AUSTRALIA

Mean Ann. Temp.　　————————　°F

Mean Ann. Temp. Ra.　————————　F°

Mean Ann. Precip.　　————————　in.

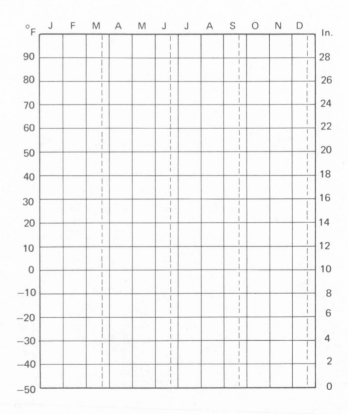

THERMOHYET DIAGRAM

SHOWING MONTHLY MEANS OF AIR TEMPERATURE
AND PRECIPITATION THROUGHOUT THE YEAR

Temperature scale is proportional to fourth power of
temperature in degrees Kelvin. Precipitation scale is
proportional to square root of precipitation depth.

Copyright © 1965 by John Wiley & Sons, Inc., New York, N.Y.

Thermohyet Diagrams

N-1. Belém, Brazil.
N-2. Cairo, U. A. R.
N-6. Antofagasta, Chile
N-7. Cairns, Australia

THERMOHYET DIAGRAM

SHOWING MONTHLY MEANS OF AIR TEMPERATURE
AND PRECIPITATION THROUGHOUT THE YEAR

Temperature scale is proportional to fourth power of
temperature in degrees Kelvin. Precipitation scale is
proportional to square root of precipitation depth.

Copyright © 1965 by John Wiley & Sons, Inc., New York, N.Y.

Thermohyet Diagrams

N-3. Akyab, Burma
N-4. Cuyaba, Brazil
N-5. Benares, India

QUESTIONS

Exercise N-1 BELÉM, BRAZIL

(a) What climate is represented by the data of Belém?

Climate name _____ Köppen code _____

(b) Compare the annual temperature range with the mean daily temperature range typical of an equatorial location. Which is the greater?

_____

_____

_____

_____

(c) Describe the annual cycle of variation in precipitation. Does this cycle correspond with the cycle of incoming solar radiation (insolation) at this latitude? (Refer to Exercise H-2.)

_____

_____

_____

_____

(d) What correlation, if any, exists between the temperature cycle and the precipitation cycle at Belém? Explain.

_____

_____

_____

_____

(e) Describe the thermohyet diagram for Belém. What climatic regime is exemplified?

_____

_____

_____

_____

Exercise N-2 CAIRO, EGYPT, U. A. R.

(a) What climate is represented by the data of Cairo?

Climate name _____ Köppen code _____

(b) Relate the annual temperature cycle of Cairo to the cycle of incoming solar radiation (insolation) at latitude 30°N. (Refer to Exercise H-2.)

_____

_____

_____

_____

(c) Compare the annual temperature range at Cairo with the mean daily temperature range typical of deserts at this latitude. Which is the larger range? Explain.

_____

_____

_____

_____

(d) Explain the marked maximum of rainfall in the January-April period and the minimum in the April-November period.

_____

_____

_____

_____

(e) What climatic regime is exhibited in the thermohyet diagram for Cairo? How are the two climatic seasons shown in the shape and position of the diagram?

_____

_____

_____

_____

_____

(f) How does it happen that Cairo, a great city of over three million population, lies in an extremely dry, tropical desert?

_____

_____

_____

(g) Name other great cities of the world that lie in true desert locations.

_____

_____

_____

Name_____ Date_____

Course No._____ Section_____

N₃

Exercise N-3 AKYAB, BURMA

(a) What climate is represented by the data of Akyab?

Climate name _____ Köppen code _____

(b) Account for the extremely high rainfall of June, July, and August. What name is given to this season?

_____

_____

_____

_____

_____

_____

(c) Notice that the annual temperature cycle has two maxima and two minima. Explain this temperature cycle.

_____

_____

_____

_____

_____

_____

(d) Describe the thermohyet diagram of Akyab. What climatic regime does it represent?

_____

_____

_____

_____

_____

153

Exercise N-4 CUYABA, BRAZIL

(a) What climate is represented by the data of Cuyaba?

Climate name _____ Köppen code _____

(b) Explain the dry season occurring in the period March through September. (Relate season to sun's path in sky.)

_____

_____

_____

_____

_____

_____

(c) Does the annual temperature cycle of Cuyaba correlate with the annual precipitation cycle? Explain.

_____

_____

_____

_____

_____

_____

(d) Compare the thermohyet diagrams of Cuyaba and Akyab. Is the regime of Cuyaba more, or less, equable than that of Akyab?

_____

_____

_____

_____

_____

_____

Exercise N-5 BENARES, INDIA

(a) What climate is represented by the data of Benares?

Climate name _____ Köppen code _____

(b) Although the climates of Akyab and Benares are closely related, there are important differences. Describe and explain the similarities and differences.

_____

_____

_____

_____

_____

(c) What is the most striking feature of the thermohyet diagram for Benares?

_____

_____

_____

_____

_____

(d) What three climatic seasons are recognizable at Benares? Label these on the thermohyet diagram.

_____

_____

_____

_____

_____

Exercise N-6 ANTOFAGASTA, CHILE

(a) What climate is represented by the data of Antofagasta?

Climate name _____ Köppen code _____

(b) What is the most obvious difference in the annual temperature cycles of Antofagasta and Cairo? Explain.

_____

_____

_____

_____

(c) How does the thermohyet diagram for Antofagasta reveal the essential climatic characteristics?

_____

_____

_____

_____

(d) What climatic regimes are combined in the thermohyet diagram of Antofagasta? Compare with Cairo.

_____

_____

_____

_____

Exercise N-7 CAIRNS, QUEENSLAND, AUSTRALIA

(a) What climate is represented by the data of Cairns?

Climate name _____ Köppen code _____

(b) Of the first six climate examples in this group, which shows the closest similarity to the climate of Cairns?

_____

_____

_____

_____

_____

(c) Explain the reduction of both temperature and precipitation in the period May through October at Cairns.

_____

_____

_____

_____

_____

_____

Group O

MIDDLE LATITUDE CLIMATES

Text References

Strahler, 1969, *Physical Geography, 3rd Edition,* Chapter 16, pp. 267–279.
Strahler, 1970, *Introduction to Physical Geography, 2nd Edition,* Chapter 11, pp. 162–170.

General Instructions

Blank climographs on following pages are to be used for plotting climate data for stations given on the reverse side of this page.

Mean monthly temperatures (°F) are to be plotted as points centered in each monthly column. The points are then connected by line segments, or by a smooth curve, showing the annual temperature cycle.

Mean monthly precipitation totals (in inches) are plotted as horizontal lines extending across the month and are joined into a step-graph.

After the data have been plotted, calculate the following values:

  (1) Mean annual temperature. (Sum of monthly means divided by 12.)

  (2) Mean annual temperature range. (Difference between highest and lowest monthly means.)

  (3) Mean annual total precipitation. (Sum of monthly means.)

Enter the above values in the blank spaces beside each climograph.

Blank thermohyet diagrams are also provided on following pages. Plot the data of each station, as was done in Exercise L-2, page 127. Label fully. Use different colored pencils, if desired, to distinguish stations having an overlap of figures.

O CLIMATE DATA

(From Trewartha and Meteorological Office of Great Britain)

Exercise O-1 BRISBANE, QUEENSLAND, AUSTRALIA, 27½°S

	J	F	M	A	M	J	J	A	S	O	N	D
Temperature, °F	77	76.5	74	70	65	60	58.5	60.5	65.5	70	73	76
Precipitation, in.	6.4	6.3	5.7	3.7	2.8	2.6	2.2	1.9	1.9	2.5	3.7	5.0

Exercise O-2 SHANNON AIRPORT, IRELAND, 52½°N

	J	F	M	A	M	J	J	A	S	O	N	D
Temperature, °F	41	42	45.5	48	52.5	58	59.5	60.5	57.5	51.5	46	42.5
Precipitation, in.	3.8	3.0	2.0	2.2	2.4	2.1	3.1	3.0	3.0	3.4	4.2	4.3

Exercise O-3 VALPARAISO, CHILE, 33°S

	J	F	M	A	M	J	J	A	S	O	N	D
Temperature, °F	67	66	65	61	59	56	55	56	58	59	62	64
Precipitation, in.	0.0	0.0	0.6	0.2	3.5	5.8	4.8	3.2	0.8	0.4	0.1	0.3

Exercise O-4 ROME, ITALY, 42°N

	J	F	M	A	M	J	J	A	S	O	N	D
Temperature, °F	45	47	51	57	64	71	76	76	70	62	53	46
Precipitation, in.	3.2	2.7	2.9	2.6	2.2	1.6	0.7	1.0	2.5	5.0	4.4	3.9

Exercise O-5 LOVELOCK, NEVADA, 40°N

	J	F	M	A	M	J	J	A	S	O	N	D
Temperature, °F	30	36	43	50	58	66	74	72	62	51	40	31
Precipitation, in.	0.7	0.5	0.4	0.4	0.4	0.3	0.2	0.2	0.3	0.4	0.3	0.4

Exercise O-6 MEDICINE HAT, ALBERTA, CANADA, 50°N

	J	F	M	A	M	J	J	A	S	O	N	D
Temperature, °F	12	14.5	28	45	55	63	69.5	66.5	56	45.5	28	19.5
Precipitation, in.	0.6	0.6	0.6	0.8	1.6	2.4	1.7	1.4	1.1	0.6	0.7	0.7

Exercise O-7 MARQUETTE, MICHIGAN, 46½°N

	J	F	M	A	M	J	J	A	S	O	N	D
Temperature, °F	16	16	25	38	49	59	65	63	57	46	33	23
Precipitation, in.	2.2	1.8	2.1	2.3	3.1	3.5	3.1	2.8	3.2	3.0	3.0	2.5

Exercise O-8 INCHON, KOREA, 37½°N

	J	F	M	A	M	J	J	A	S	O	N	D
Temperature, °F	26	29	38	50	59.5	68.5	75	77.5	68.5	58	43.5	30.5
Precipitation, in.	0.8	0.7	1.2	2.6	3.3	3.9	10.9	8.8	4.3	1.6	1.6	1.1

CLIMOGRAPHS

Exercise O-1 BRISBANE, AUSTRALIA

Mean Ann. Temp.   _____ °F

Mean Ann. Temp. Ra. _____ F°

Mean Ann. Precip.   _____ in.

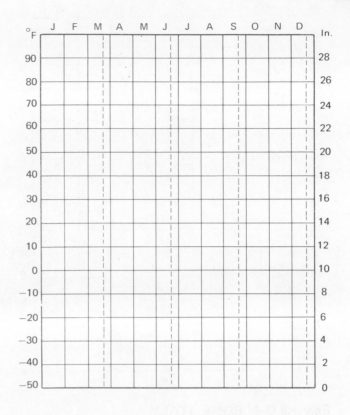

Exercise O-2 SHANNON AIR-PORT, IRELAND

Mean Ann. Temp.   _____ °F

Mean Ann. Temp. Ra. _____ F°

Mean Ann. Precip.   _____ in.

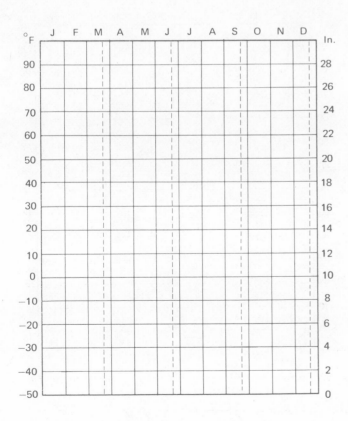

O3, 4

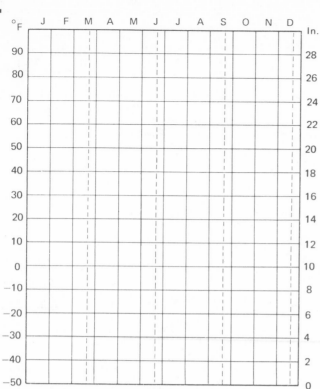

Exercise O-3 VALPARAISO, CHILE

Mean Ann. Temp. _____ °F

Mean Ann. Temp. Ra. _____ F°

Mean Ann. Precip. _____ in.

Exercise O-4 ROME, ITALY

Mean Ann. Temp. _____ °F

Mean Ann. Temp. Ra. _____ F°

Mean Ann. Precip. _____ in.

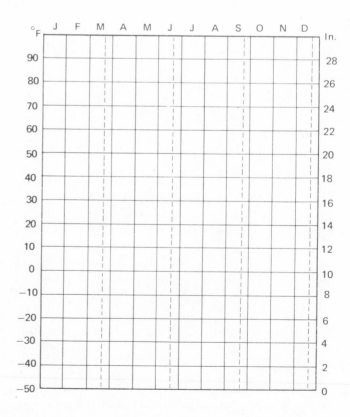

Exercise O-5 LOVELOCK, NEVADA

Mean Ann. Temp.   _____ °F

Mean Ann. Temp. Ra. _____ F°

Mean Ann. Precip.   _____ in.

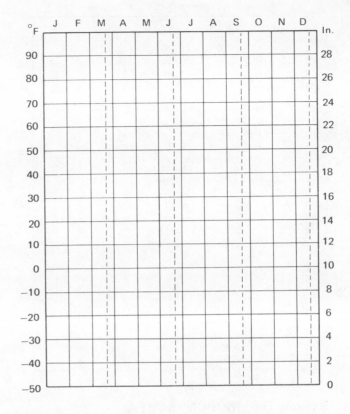

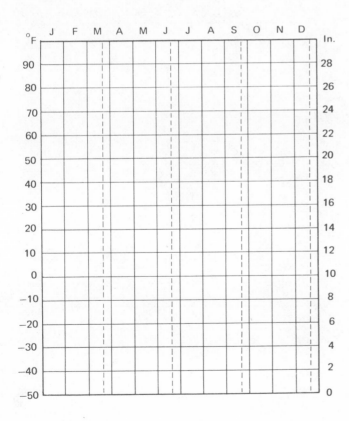

Exercise O-6 MEDICINE HAT, ALBERTA

Mean Ann. Temp.   _____ °F

Mean Ann. Temp. Ra. _____ F°

Mean Ann. Precip.   _____ in.

O$_{7,8}$

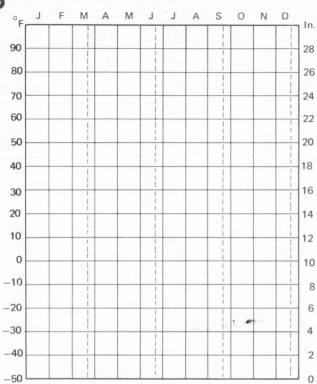

Exercise O-7 MARQUETTE, MICHIGAN

Mean Ann. Temp.   _____ °F

Mean Ann. Temp. Ra.   _____ F°

Mean Ann. Precip.   _____ in.

Exercise O-8 INCHON, KOREA

Mean Ann. Temp.   _____ °F

Mean Ann. Temp. Ra.   _____ F°

Mean Ann. Precip.   _____ in.

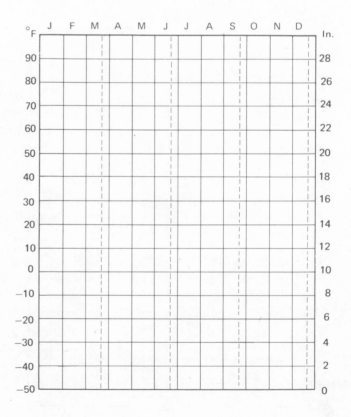

O1, 2, 3, 4

THERMOHYET DIAGRAM

SHOWING MONTHLY MEANS OF AIR TEMPERATURE
AND PRECIPITATION THROUGHOUT THE YEAR

Temperature scale is proportional to fourth power of
temperature in degrees Kelvin. Precipitation scale is
proportional to square root of precipitation depth.

Copyright © 1965 by John Wiley & Sons, Inc., New York, N.Y.

Thermohyet Diagrams

O-1   Brisbane, Queensland
O-2   Shannon Airport, Ireland
O-3   Valparaiso, Chile
O-4   Rome, Italy

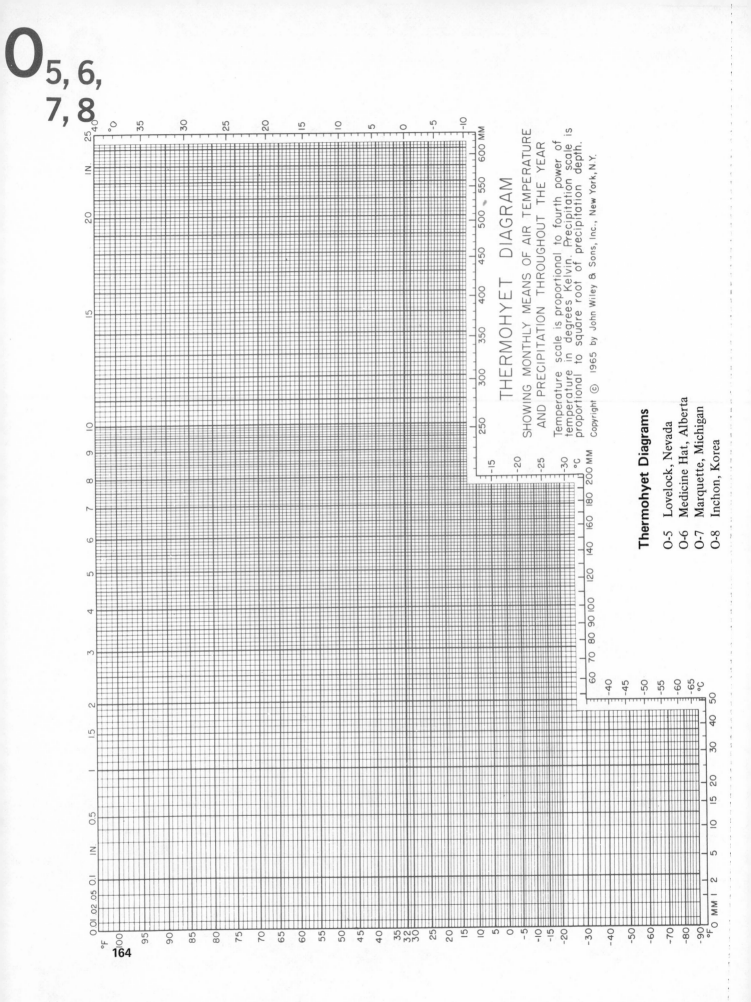

THERMOHYET DIAGRAM

SHOWING MONTHLY MEANS OF AIR TEMPERATURE
AND PRECIPITATION THROUGHOUT THE YEAR

Temperature scale is proportional to fourth power of
temperature in degrees Kelvin. Precipitation scale is
proportional to square root of precipitation depth.

Copyright © 1965 by John Wiley & Sons, Inc., New York, N.Y.

Thermohyet Diagrams

O-5   Lovelock, Nevada
O-6   Medicine Hat, Alberta
O-7   Marquette, Michigan
O-8   Inchon, Korea

QUESTIONS

Exercise O-1 BRISBANE, QUEENSLAND, AUSTRALIA

(a) What climate is represented by the data of Brisbane?

Climate name _____ Köppen code _____

(b) Compare the annual cycles of temperature and precipitation at Brisbane with those of a corresponding station along the Atlantic seaboard of the United States (e.g., Charleston, South Carolina). Describe and explain the differences.

_____

_____

_____

_____

_____

_____

_____

_____

_____

_____

(c) Describe the thermohyet diagram of Brisbane. What climatic regime is dominant?

_____

_____

_____

_____

_____

(d) How does the thermohyet diagram show the effect of a vast ocean poleward of the Australian landmass, as constrasted with a vast landmass poleward of corresponding climate areas of North America and Asia?

_____

_____

_____

_____

_____

O 1, 2

(e) In what respect would the related climates of the China coast (e.g., Shanghai) and southern Japan (e.g., Nagasaki) differ from the climate of Brisbane? Explain.

_____

_____

_____

_____

Exercise O-2 SHANNON AIRPORT, IRELAND

(a) What climate is represented by the data of Shannon Airport?

Climate name _____ Köppen code _____

(b) How does the windward coastal location of Shannon Airport affect the temperature and precipitation cycles, as seen in the climograph?

_____

_____

_____

_____

_____

(c) Explain the marked decrease in monthly precipitation during the period March through June.

_____

_____

_____

_____

_____

(d) Describe the thermohyet diagram for Shannon Airport. How does the diagram reflect equability of climatic regime?

_____

_____

_____

_____

(e) What other climatic regime, beside the middle-latitude equable regime, is seen in the thermohyet diagram of Shannon Airport?

_____

_____

_____

Exercise O-3 VALPARAISO, CHILE

(a) What climate is represented by the data of Valparaiso?

Climate name _____ Köppen code _____

(b) What major cities of the United States would be expected to have climographs closely similar to that of Valparaiso?

_____

(c) What African city would be expected to have a climate closely similar to Valparaiso's?

_____

(d) In what way does the thermohyet diagram of Valparaiso show the equability of a marine environment?

_____
_____
_____
_____
_____

Exercise O-4 ROME, ITALY

(a) What climate is represented by the data of Rome?

Climate name _____ Köppen code _____

(b) In what important respects does the climate of Rome differ from that of Valparaiso? Explain the differences.

_____
_____
_____
_____
_____
_____
_____
_____
_____

04

(c) Compare the thermohyet diagram of Rome with that of Valparaiso, particularly with respect to equability of temperatures.

_____

_____

_____

_____

_____

(d) How does the Köppen system recognize the differences between the climate of Rome and that of Valparaiso?

_____

_____

_____

_____

_____

_____

_____

_____

Exercise O-5 LOVELOCK, NEVADA

(a) What climate is represented by the data of Lovelock?

Climate name _____ Köppen code _____

(b) Compare the climate of Lovelock with that of Cairo, U. A. R. (Exercise N-2). How do the temperature cycles differ? Explain.

_____

_____

_____

_____

_____

_____

(c) Does the precipitation cycle at Lovelock show the influence of a location on the western margin of the continent? Explain. (Refer to climographs of Shannon Airport, Ireland, and Rome, Italy.)

_____

_____

_____

_____

_____

_____

Exercise O-6 MEDICINE HAT, ALBERTA

(a) What climate is represented by the data of Medicine Hat?

Climate name _____ Köppen code _____

(b) Explain the large annual temperature range at Medicine Hat.

_____

_____

_____

_____

(c) What is the source of moisture for the summer precipitation at Medicine Hat?

_____

_____

_____

_____

O7 Exercise O-7 MARQUETTE, MICHIGAN

(a) What climate is represented by the data of Marquette?

Climate name _____ Köppen code _____

(b) Explain the fact that Marquette has a rather uniform precipitation throughout the year, with winter amounts only slightly less than in summer. (Consider relationship to Great Lakes.)

_____

_____

_____

_____

_____

(c) Compare the thermohyet diagram of Marquette with that of Medicine Hat. What regime is illustrated? How are differences in precipitation cycles and amounts reflected in the thermohyet diagrams?

_____

_____

_____

_____

_____

_____

Exercise O-8 INCHON, KOREA

(a) What climate is represented by the data of Inchon?

Climate name _____ Köppen code _____

(b) The temperature cycle of Inchon closely resembles that of Omaha, Nebraska, but the precipitation cycles differ strikingly for the summer months. Describe and explain this difference.

_____

_____

_____

_____

_____

(c) Describe the thermohyet diagram of Inchon. What climatic regimes are combined in this climate?

_____

_____

_____

Group P

POLAR, ARCTIC, AND HIGHLAND CLIMATES

P

Text References

Strahler, 1969, *Physical Geography, 3rd Edition*, Chapter 17, pp. 281–293.
Strahler, 1970, *Introduction to Physical Geography, 2nd Edition*, Chapter 12, pp. 172–184.

General Instructions

Black climographs on following pages are to be used for plotting climate data for stations given on the reverse side of this page.

Mean monthly temperatures (°F) are to be plotted as points centered in each monthly column. The points are then connected by line segments, or by a smooth curve, showing the annual temperature cycle.

Mean monthly precipitation totals (in inches) are plotted as horizontal lines extending across the month and are joined into a step-graph.

After the data have been plotted, calculate the following values:

(1) Mean annual temperature. (Sum of monthly means divided by 12.)

(2) Mean annual temperature range. (Difference between highest and lowest monthly means.)

(3) Mean annual total precipitation. (Sum of monthly means.)

Enter the above values in the blank spaces beside each climograph.

Blank thermohyet diagrams are also provided on following pages. Plot the data of each station, as was done in Exercise L-2, page 127. Label fully. Use different colored pencils, if desired, to distinguish stations having an overlap of figures.

CLIMATE DATA

(From Trewartha and Meteorological Office of Great Britain)

Exercise P-1 Verkhoyansk, U. S. S. R., 67½°N

	J	F	M	A	M	J	J	A	S	O	N	D
Temperature, °F	−58.5	−48.5	−26	4.5	32.5	54	56.5	49	35	4.5	−35.5	−54
Precipitation, in.	0.2	0.1	0.1	0.2	0.3	0.9	1.0	1.0	0.5	0.4	0.3	0.1

Exercise P-2 VARDØ, NORWAY, 70°N

	J	F	M	A	M	J	J	A	S	O	N	D
Temperature, °F	23	22	24.5	30	36	42.5	48.5	48.5	43.5	35	29.5	26
Precipitation, in.	2.5	2.5	2.3	1.5	1.3	1.3	1.5	1.7	1.9	2.5	2.1	2.4

Exercise P-3 POINT BARROW, ALASKA, 71°N

	J	F	M	A	M	J	J	A	S	O	N	D
Temperature, °F	−15.5	−18.5	−15	−0.5	18.5	34	39.5	38.5	30.5	17	1	−10.5
Precipitation, in.	0.2	0.1	0.1	0.1	0.1	0.3	0.9	0.8	0.5	0.5	0.3	0.2

Exercise P-4 KODAIKANAL, INDIA, 10°N, ELEVATION 7700 FT.

	J	F	M	A	M	J	J	A	S	O	N	D
Temperature, °F	55	56	59	61	62	59	58	58	58	57	55	55
Precipitation, in.	2.9	1.4	2.0	4.3	6.0	4.1	5.0	7.0	7.3	9.7	8.2	4.4

Exercise P-5 LHASA, TIBET, 29½°N, ELEVATION 12,090 FT.

	J	F	M	A	M	J	J	A	S	O	N	D
Temperature, °F	29	34	40.5	46.5	54	62	61.5	60	57.5	48	39	32
Precipitation, in.	<0.1	0.5	0.3	0.2	1.0	2.5	4.8	3.5	2.6	0.5	0.1	0.0

CLIMOGRAPHS

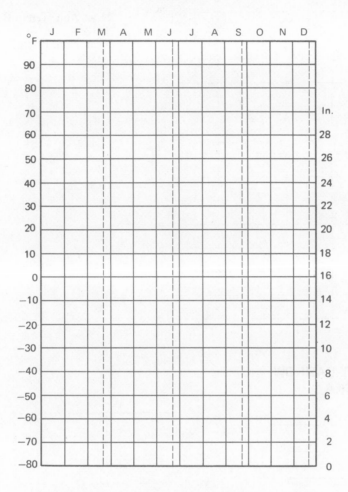

Exercise P-1 VERKHOYANSK, U. S. S. R.

Mean Ann. Temp.   _____ °F

Mean Ann. Temp. Ra.   _____ F°

Mean Ann. Precip.   _____ in.

P_{2,3}

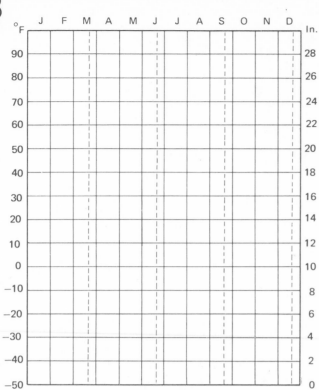

Exercise P-2 VARDØ, NORWAY

Mean Ann. Temp.   _____ °F

Mean Ann. Temp. Ra. _____ F°

Mean Ann. Precip.   _____ in.

Exercise P-3 POINT BARROW, ALASKA

Mean Ann. Temp.   _____ °F

Mean Ann. Temp. Ra. _____ F°

Mean Ann. Precip.   _____ in.

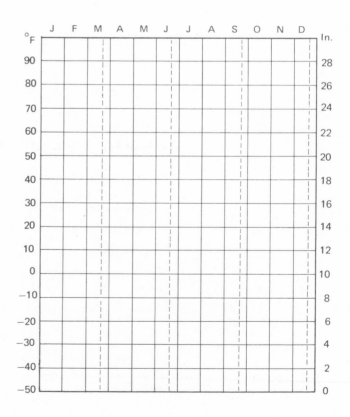

Exercise P-4 KODAIKANAL, INDIA

Mean Ann. Temp. _____ °F

Mean Ann. Temp. Ra. _____ F°

Mean Ann. Precip. _____ in.

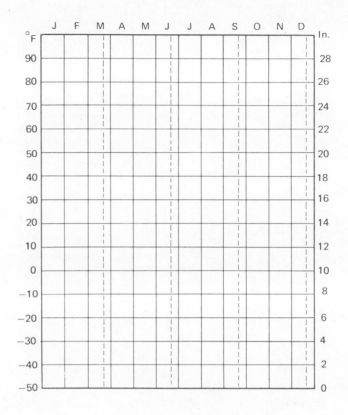

Exercise P-5 LHASA, TIBET

Mean Ann. Temp. _____ °F

Mean Ann. Temp. Ra. _____ F°

Mean Ann. Precip. _____ in.

P

Station:

_____

Mean Ann. Temp.   _____ °F

Mean Ann. Temp. Ra.   _____ F°

Mean Ann. Precip.   _____ in.

Station:

_____

Mean Ann. Temp.   _____ °F

Mean Ann. Temp. Ra.   _____ F°

Mean Ann. Precip.   _____ in.

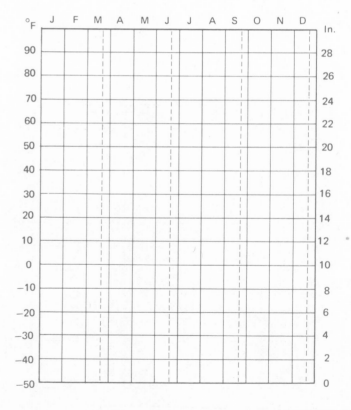

THERMOHYET DIAGRAM

SHOWING MONTHLY MEANS OF AIR TEMPERATURE AND PRECIPITATION THROUGHOUT THE YEAR

Temperature scale is proportional to fourth power of temperature in degrees Kelvin. Precipitation scale is proportional to square root of precipitation depth.

Copyright © 1965 by John Wiley & Sons, Inc., New York, N.Y.

Thermohyet Diagrams

P-1   Verkhoyansk, U. S. S. R.
P-2   Vardø, Norway
P-3   Point Barrow, Alaska

P 4, 5

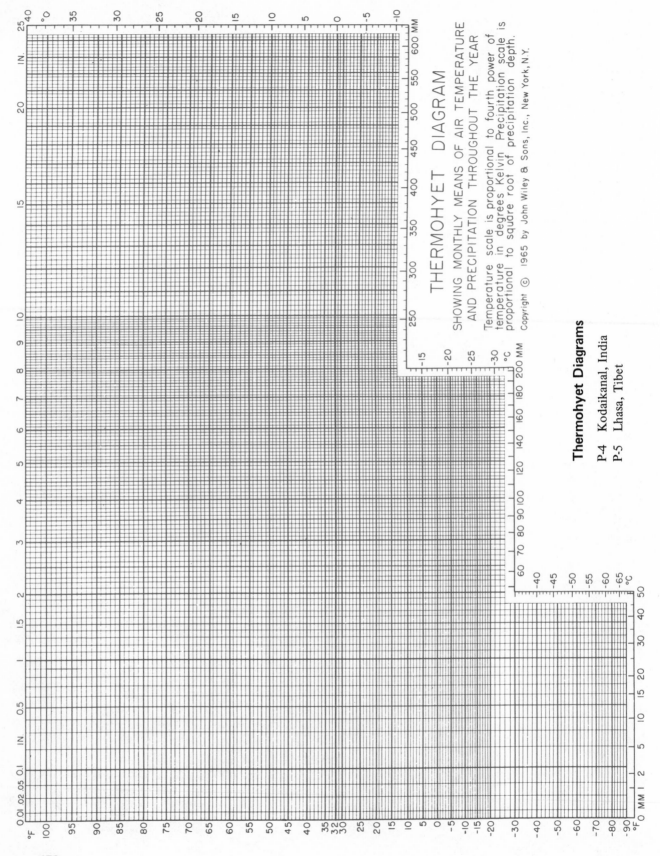

THERMOHYET DIAGRAM

SHOWING MONTHLY MEANS OF AIR TEMPERATURE
AND PRECIPITATION THROUGHOUT THE YEAR

Temperature scale is proportional to fourth power of
temperature in degrees Kelvin. Precipitation scale is
proportional to square root of precipitation depth.

Copyright © 1965 by John Wiley & Sons, Inc., New York, N.Y.

Thermohyet Diagrams

P-4   Kodaikanal, India
P-5   Lhasa, Tibet

178

QUESTIONS

Exercise P-1 VERKHOYANSK, U. S. S. R.

(a) What climate is represented by the data of Verkhoyansk?

Climate name _____ Köppen code _____

(b) Explain why the annual range of temperature in this climate exceeds that of the ice-cap climate (EF) of Greenland and Antarctica.

_____

_____

_____

_____

_____

(c) Which two-month period of the year shows the greatest change in monthly mean temperature? Calculate for four periods:

Feb.-March-April	_____ F°	Sept.-Oct.-Nov.	_____ F°
March-April-May	_____ F°	Oct.-Nov.-Dec.	_____ F°

(d) How do the precipitation cycle and annual total at Verkhoyansk differ from corresponding values for a comparable station in North America (e.g., Dawson, Yukon Territory)? Explain.

_____

_____

_____

_____

_____

(e) Describe the thermohyet diagram for Verkhoyansk. What two climatic regimes are combined in this diagram?

_____

_____

_____

_____

_____

_____

2 Exercise P-2 VARDØ, NORWAY

(a) What climate is represented by the data of Vardø?

Climate name _____ Köppen code _____

(b) Explain the comparatively small annual temperature range at Vardø, as compared with that at Verkhoyansk, although Vardø is situated at an even higher latitude than Verkhoyansk.

_____

_____

_____

_____

_____

_____

(c) Compare the annual precipitation cycle at Vardø with that at Shannon Airport, Ireland (Exercise O-2).
In what way are these cycles similar, and why?

_____

_____

_____

_____

_____

_____

_____

_____

_____

(d) Compare the thermohyet diagram of Vardø with that of Shannon Airport, Ireland (Exercise O-2). How
closely are they related? What climatic regime is shown?

_____

_____

_____

_____

_____

_____

_____

Exercise P-3 POINT BARROW, ALASKA

(a) What climate is represented by the data of Point Barrow?

Climate name _____ Köppen code _____

(b) Compare annual temperature range at Point Barrow with that at Verkhoyansk. Then compare with the range at Vardø. Explain Point Barrow's annual range in terms of the other two stations.

_____

_____

_____

_____

_____

_____

_____

_____

(c) Are the annual precipitation cycle and total at Point Barrow more closely related to corresponding data for Verkhoyansk, or to data for Vardø? Explain.

_____

_____

_____

_____

_____

_____

_____

_____

(d) Describe the thermohyet diagram for Point Barrow in relation to the diagrams for Verkhoyansk and Vardø. Which affiliation is the closer?

_____

_____

_____

_____

_____

_____

_____

Exercise P-4 KODAIKANAL, INDIA

(a) Compare the mean annual temperature of Kodaikanal with that of a sea-level station in the same area (e.g., Cochin, India). Give both values and the difference.

_____

_____

(b) Using the temperature difference in (a), calculate the temperature drop in degrees per 1000 feet between sea level and Kodaikanal.

_____

Is the lapse rate you have calculated more or less than the normal temperature lapse rate of 3½ F° per 1000 ft.?

_____

(c) What climatic regime is shown by the thermohyet diagram for Kodaikanal?

_____

_____

_____

Exercise P-5 LHASA, TIBET

(a) Compare the annual temperature range of Lhasa with that of a north-Indian station at low elevation (e.g., Allahabad, India). Give both values and the difference.

_____

_____

_____

_____

(b) Compare the thermohyet diagram of Lhasa with that of either Benares (Exercise N-5) or Allahabad. In what respects are the diagrams similar in form?

_____

_____

_____

_____

In what respects are the thermohyet diagrams different?

_____

_____

_____

_____

_____

Group Q

SOIL TEXTURES

Q

Text References

Strahler, 1969, *Physical Geography, 3rd Edition,* Chapter 18, pp. 295–306.
Strahler, 1970, *Introduction to Physical Geography, 2nd Edition,* Chapter 13, pp. 187–188.

Table of Soil Texture Grades
(U. S. Department of Agriculture)

Name of Grade	Diameter (Inches)	Diameter (Millimeters)
Coarse gravel	Above 0.08	Above 2
Fine gravel	0.04 — 0.08	1 — 2
Coarse sand	0.02 — 0.04	0.5 — 1
Medium sand	0.01 — 0.02	0.25 — 0.5
Fine sand	0.004 — 0.01	0.1 — 0.25
Very fine sand	0.002 — 0.004	0.05 — 0.1
Silt	0.000,08 — 0.002	0.002 — 0.05
Clay	Below 0.000,08	Below 0.002

Soil Texture Diagram*

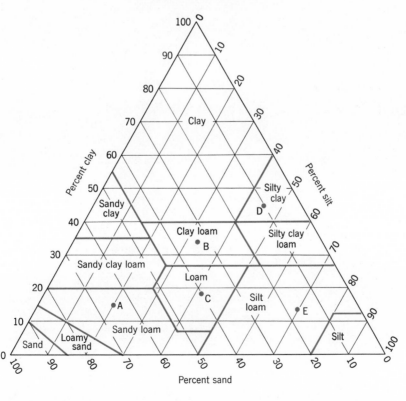

*From U. S. Department of Agriculture and C. E. Millar, L. M. Turk, and H. D. Foth, *Fundamentals of Soil Science,* John Wiley and Sons, 1965, New York.

Pie diagrams of samples shown on
triangular diagram, page 183.

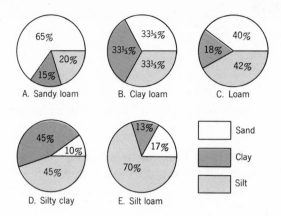

A. Sandy loam — 65%, 20%, 15%

B. Clay loam — 33⅓%, 33⅓%, 33⅓%

C. Loam — 40%, 42%, 18%

D. Silty clay — 45%, 10%, 45%

E. Silt loam — 13%, 17%, 70%

Sand

Clay

Silt

Exercise Q-1 SOIL TEXTURE GRADES

Soil texture grades as defined by the U. S. Department of Agriculture are given in the table on page 183.

On the blank graph below, locate the size limits of each grade. Draw a vertical line at each limit from bottom to top of the graph. Label the line with the diameter in millimeters. Then label each size grade with initials as follows:

Clay (and finer)	C−
Silt	S
Very fine sand	VFS
Fine sand	FS
Medium sand	MS
Coarse sand	CS
Fine gravel	FG
Coarse gravel and coarser	CG+

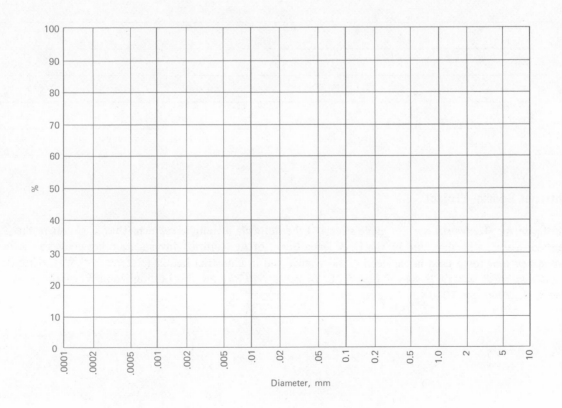

(Go on to questions on reverse side of page)

Q1 Exercise Q-1 *(continued)*

(a) Examine the horizontal scale used on the graph. What name is applied to a scale of this type?

_____

(b) Medium sand, coarse sand, and fine sand have the following size limits: 0.25, 0.5, 1.0, and 2.0 mm. What mathematical term is applied to a succession of numbers related in this manner?

_____

What ratio of increase holds constant in the above number succession?

_____

(c) Does a point of zero value exist on the horizontal scale to the left of the graph, assuming the graph to be extended in that direction? Explain.

_____

_____

_____

(d) Using the data of the pie-diagrams on page 184, plot the percentages of each texture grade on the graph on page 185. Represent the percentage of each grade by a horizontal line drawn across the zone covered by the grade. Use a different color or line pattern for each example. Label with letters A, B, C, etc.

(e) Suggest a way in which the size grade limits might be altered to result in a more uniform system.

_____

_____

_____

_____

_____

_____

Optional Special Project

Investigate the *Wentworth scale* of grade sizes and the *Phi-scale* of numbers which it uses. Compare the Wentworth scale with that used by the U. S. Department of Agriculture. Investigate other grade-size scale systems, such as those used in engineering soil science and in industrial fields. (References: W. C. Krumbein, *J. Sedimentary Petrology,* 8, 84–90 (1938); L. D. Baver, *Soil Physics,* 3rd Edition, John Wiley and Sons, New York, 1956, pp. 10–18.)

Exercise Q-2 SOIL TEXTURE CLASS LIMITS

Refer to the triangular soil-texture diagram on page 183. Names of texture classes and boundaries are shown. Estimate the limiting percentages of sand, silt, and clay that define each of the twelve texture classes. Enter the percentages in the table below:

Class Name		Sand (%)	Silt (%)	Clay (%)
Sand				
Loamy sand				
Sandy loam				
Sandy clay loam				
Loam	(Example)	43 – 52	28 – 50	7 – 27
Silt loam				
Silt				
Silty clay loam				
Clay loam				
Sandy clay				
Silty clay				
Clay				

Q3 Exercise Q-3 IDENTIFICATION OF SOIL TEXTURE CLASSES

Given in the table below are percentages of sand, silt, and clay in each of five soil samples:

Sample No.	Sand (%)	Silt (%)	Clay (%)
1	15	51	34
2	72	14	14
3	10	85	5
4	18	32	50
5	47	32	21

(a) Locate each sample on the triangular diagram on page 183. Make a dot, surrounded by a small circle, and label with the sample number. In the spaces below, write the name of the soil texture class.

Sample 1 _____

Sample 2 _____

Sample 3 _____

Sample 4 _____

Sample 5 _____

(b) Using the blank circles below, construct a pie-diagram of each of the five samples. (Refer to examples on page 184.)

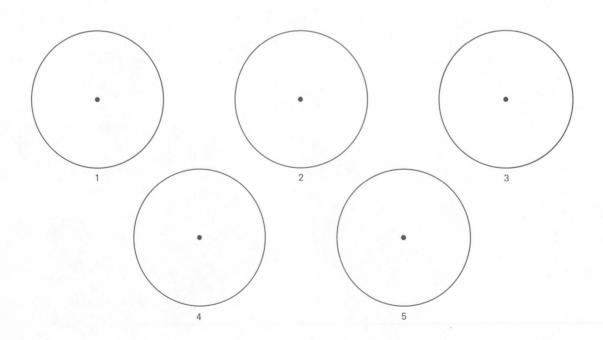

Group R

MAP READING AND TOPOGRAPHIC CONTOURS

Text References

Strahler, 1969, *Physical Geography, 3rd Edition,* Appendix I, pp. 621–641.
Strahler, 1970, *Introduction to Physical Geography, 2nd Edition,* Appendix II, pp. 426–431.

Map for use in Exercise R-1.

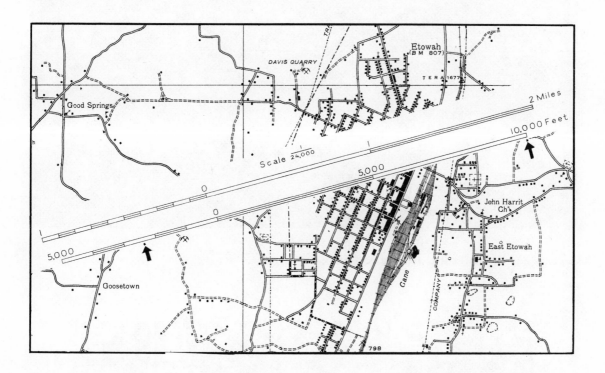

Air photograph for Exercise R-2. (Photograph by U. S. Department of Agriculture.)
Pasadena, California, July 1938.

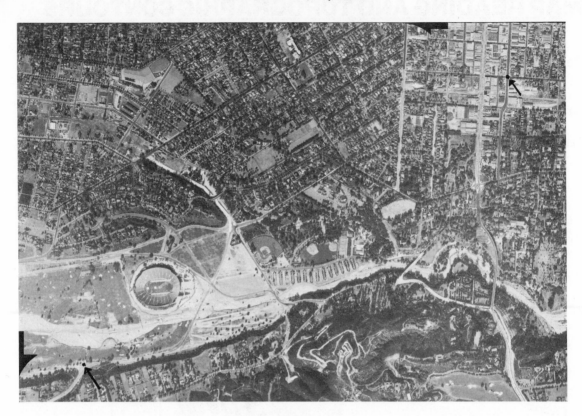

Topographic map for Exercise R-2. (From U. S. Geological Survey)

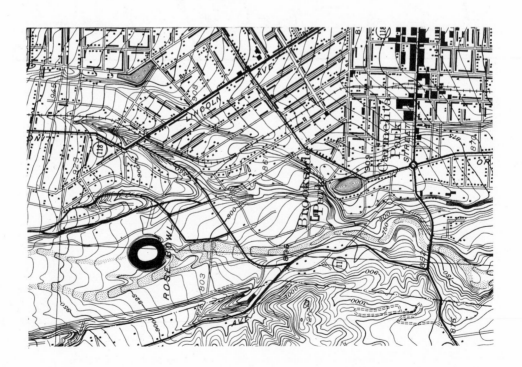

Name_____ Date_____

Course No._____ Section_____ **R₁**

Exercise R-1 MAP SCALES AND DISTANCES

Refer to the map on page 189. This map was originally printed on a scale of 1:24,000, but has been reduced for printing here.

(a) What is the fractional scale of the map, as printed on page 189? Show computations.

_____

(b) Determine the width and length (in miles) of the area shown by the map. (Estimate to nearest 0.01 mi.)

Length _____ mi Width _____ mi

(c) Determine the distance in yards from Davis quarry to John Harrit Church.

_____ yd

(d) Prepare a graphic scale in kilometers for this map. Mark the scale on the line below. Show computations. Subdivide the scale to the left of the zero mark into tenths of a kilometer.

0

(e) State the scale of the map in inches to miles.

Scale: _____ inch equals _____ mi

Determine the true bearing of a line from John Harrit Church to Davis quarry. Give both full-circle bearing and compass-quadrant bearing.

Full-circle bearing _____ °

Compass-quadrant bearing _____

(f) Determine the full-circle bearing and distance in feet between the two points marked by heavy black arrows on the graphic scale.

Bearing _____ ° Distance _____ yd

R₂ Exercise R-2 AIR PHOTOGRAPH SCALE

Refer to the air photograph reproduced on page 190.

(a) The horizontal ground distance between points shown by the two arrows on the photograph was measured by ground survey. The distance is 1.74 miles. What is the fractional scale of the photograph? Show computations.

R. F. _____

(b) Construct an equivalent graphic scale in 1000-yard units. Subdivide the scale to the left of the zero point into 100-yard units. Show computations.

0

(c) Construct an equivalent scale in meters. Show computations.

0

(d) Assuming that the air photograph is of constant linear scale in all directions over the entire area shown, calculate the area shown in the photograph. Give answer in square miles and square kilometers.

Length _____ mi _____ km Area _____ sq mi

Width _____ mi _____ km Area _____ sq km

(e) The topographic map on page 190 covers the same area as the air photograph, but is printed on a different scale. Determine the scale of the map and state as a representative fraction.

R. F. _____

R₃

Exercise R-3 CONTOUR MAPS OF GEOMETRIC FIGURES

Show by topographic contours alone each of the following geometric solids, assumed to be resting on a horizontal plane. Construct the maps carefully, using a pencil compass and straightedge.

(a) Straight-sided cone.

(b) Cone with sides concave-up.

+

+

(c) Hemisphere.

(d) Cube.

+

R4 Exercise R-4 CONTOUR MAP OF IMAGINARY ISLAND

In the blank space on this page, draw a contour map of a semicircular island, the straight side of which has a very steep slope as compared with the remainder of the island. The summit point of the island is 105 ft above sea level. The contour interval is 10 ft. Two stream valleys extend down the gently sloping sides of the island. The island is about 5 mi wide. Use a map scale of one inch to one mile.

Exercise R-5 DRAWING TOPOGRAPHIC CONTOURS

(a) Complete the drawing of contours at intervals of 100 ft on the map below. Use soft pencil and draw lightly at first. Then go over the lines in heavy pencil or ink. See questions on page 198.

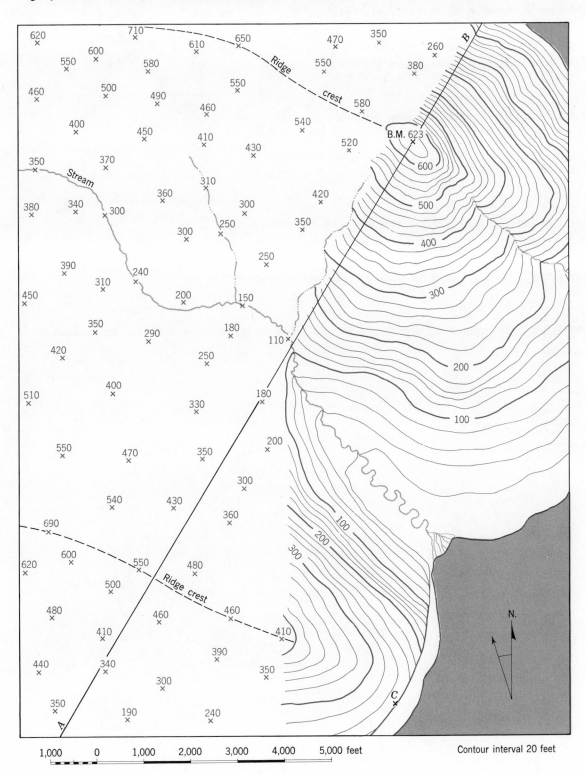

Contour interval 20 feet

R6 QUESTIONS

Refer to the contour topographic map on page 197.

(a) What is the contour interval used on the map?

_____ ft

(b) Give the elevation of the contour at point A.

_____ ft

(c) Give the elevation of the contour at point B.

_____ ft

(d) Estimate the elevation of summit point C.

_____ ft

(e) Estimate the elevation of the point D.

_____ ft

(f) Give the elevation of the hachured depression contour at E.

_____ ft

(g) Estimate the elevation of the bottom of the depression at point F.

_____ ft

(h) Estimate the depth of the depression floor as F below the lowest point of the rim that encloses it.

_____ ft

Exercise R-6 DETERMINING ELEVATIONS FROM A CONTOUR MAP

Answer questions on page 196 relating to the map below.

(b) Construct a profile along the line $A-B$, using the graph on this page. Fold the page under on the line indicated and attach the folded edge to the profile line $A-B$ on the map on page 195.

Use a vertical exaggeration of five times the horizontal scale. Label elevations at 100-ft intervals on the vertical scale.

(c) How high is the cliff at Point C in the south-eastern part of the map?

_____ ft

(d) What is the amount and direction of magnetic declination in this area?

_____

(e) Determine the slope of the ground, in feet per mile, along the profile line between the 200 and 500 foot contour lines in the northeastern part of the map.

_____ ft per mi

(f) Convert the answer to (e) into degrees of arc, measured from the horizontal.

_____ °

(g) Convert the answer to (e) into percent of grade.

_____ %

Fold page under along this line

Profile for Exercise R-5.

Group S

THE WASTING OF SLOPES

Text References

Strahler, 1969, *Physical Geography, 3rd Edition*, Chapter 24, pp. 395–413.
Strahler, 1970, *Introduction to Physical Geography, 2nd Edition*, Chapter 19, pp. 275–286.

Exercise S-1 EXFOLIATION DOMES (Source: Yosemite National Park, Calif., U. S. Geological Survey topographic map: scale 1:24,000.)

EXPLANATORY NOTE: North Dome and Basket Dome, two great exfoliation domes of massive granitic intrusive rock, rise above the northwest wall of Tenaya Canyon, a branch of Yosemite Valley. These domes are seen in the photograph below, viewed from the south. In the southeastern part of this map is the floor of Tenaya Canyon, a deeply scoured glacial trough. Much rock was removed from the northwest wall of Tenaya Canyon by ice of the Wisconsin glacial stage, causing steep, irregular cliffs. North Dome and Basket Dome, lying above the level of this glacier, escaped modification.

The remarkable fidelity of contours on this map is a tribute to the great topographer-geologist, Francois E. Matthes, who not only surveyed the area and drew the map, but who also published a comprehensive volume on the geologic history of Yosemite Valley*.

*Matthes, F. E. (1930), Geologic History of Yosemite Valley, *U. S. Geol. Survey Prof. Paper* 160, 137 pp. See pp. 114-116.

Map to accompany Exercise S-1. Elevations are in feet.

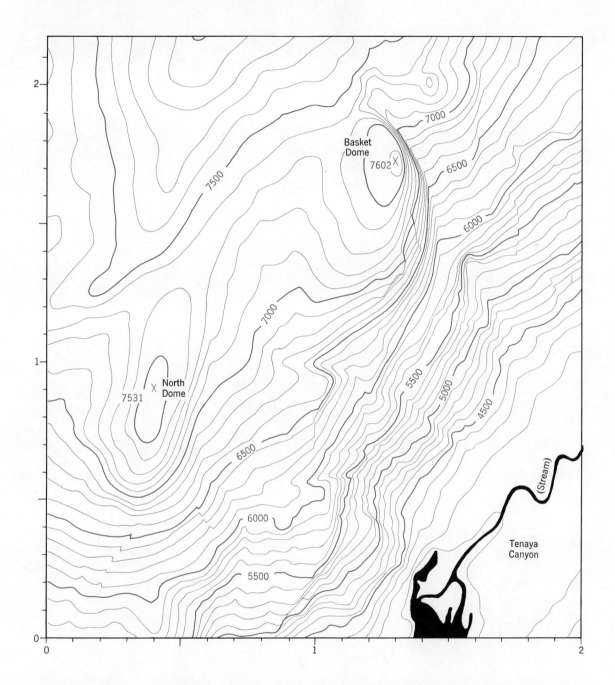

On all contour maps used in this and following exercises, a 1000-yard grid system is marked on the margins of the maps. Locations of places will be given in grid coordinates. The first number gives distance to right from lower left-hand corner; the second number gives distance up from bottom line. For example, in the map above, the grid coordinates of North Dome are 0.4–0.9, meaning "Right 400 yards; Up 900 yards." (Reference: Strahler, 1969, *Physical Geography, 3rd Edition,* Chapter 3, p. 57 and Figure 3.14.)

Exercise S-1 QUESTIONS (show computations)

(a) What contour interval is used on this map?   Ans._____

(b) What is the difference in elevation between the summit of Basket Dome and the floor of Tenaya Canyon?

       Elevation of Basket Dome   _____ ft

       Elevation of lowest contour in Tenaya Canyon   _____ ft

                 Difference   _____ ft (Answer)

(c) Calculate the angle of slope of the southwest side of Basket Dome between 7300 and 7500 feet elevation. Use the graphic method. Construct a triangle on the graph paper below. Measure the angle of slope directly with a protractor.
       Ans._____°

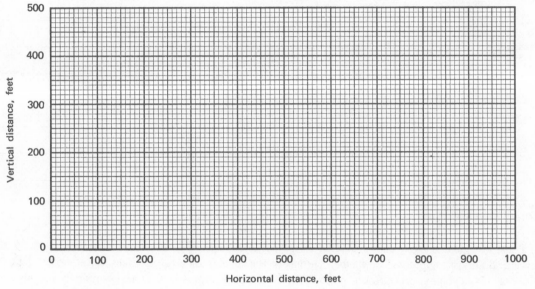

(d) Calculate the angle of slope of the steepest part of the northeast face of Basket Dome. Use the graph paper above.
       Ans._____°

(e) Can you give a geological reason for the fact that Basket Dome is highly unsymmetrical, whereas North Dome is highly symmetrical?

_____

_____

_____

_____

_____

_____

S 1

(f) Explain the curious angular zigzag bends in the contours at 0.6—0.4 and 0.2—0.2. Examine the accompanying photograph closely. Relate details of the photograph to map details.

_____

_____

_____

_____

_____

_____

_____

(g) Note that the topography of the wall of Tenaya Canyon below 6500 ft elevation is steep, rough, and blocky in comparison with the smooth, broadly rounded slopes at higher elevation. Offer an explanation for this contrast.

_____

_____

_____

_____

_____

_____

_____

Optional Map Exercise

Using a soft lead pencil, apply plastic shading to the contour map. Assume oblique illumination from the northwest. Southeast slopes will be shaded. Intensify the shading on steeper slopes. (Reference: Strahler, 1969, *Physical Geography, 3rd Edition,* pp. 630—631. Study Figure A I.10 as an example of a shaded relief map. Alternate reference: Strahler, 1965, *Introduction to Physical Geography,* pp. 422, 424.)

Exercise S-2 LANDSLIDE (Source: Map 57A, Frank, Alta., Geological Survey of Canada; scale 1:9,600.)

EXPLANATORY NOTE: The great Turtle Mountain landslide of April 29, 1903, is shown on this map, modified from a special large-scale map made during an investigation of the cause of the disastrous slide, which wiped out a part of the town of Frank, Alberta, taking the lives of 70 persons. The block diagram below shows the area of the map and includes a geological cross section.

Between North Peak and South Peak, on Turtle Mountain, a great mass of limestone slid away, descending about 2500 ft to the Crow's Nest River. As the rock mass disintegrated into rubble, a flowage movement developed; the momentum of the 35 to 40 million cubic yards of material was so great as to carry some debris 400 ft above river level on the east side of the valley.

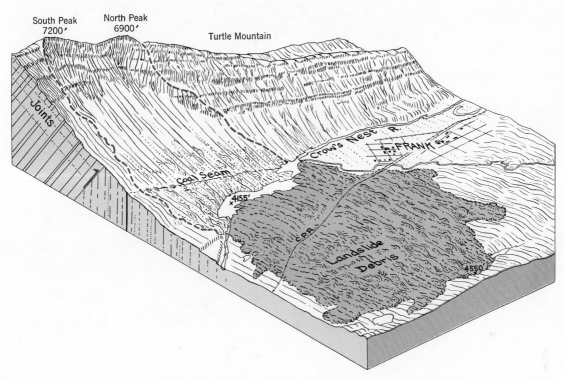

CUT HERE

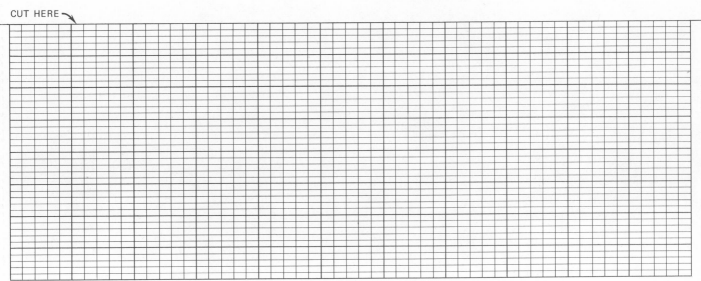

205

Exercise S-2 (continued)

On this map, limits of the slide are shown by a dashed line. Contour interval is reduced within the area of debris east of the river in order to show details of the topography. Series of dashed lines on Turtle Mountain in the vicinity of 0.3−0.7 represent open cracks, or fissures, in the limestone, which are fractures produced at the time of the landslide.

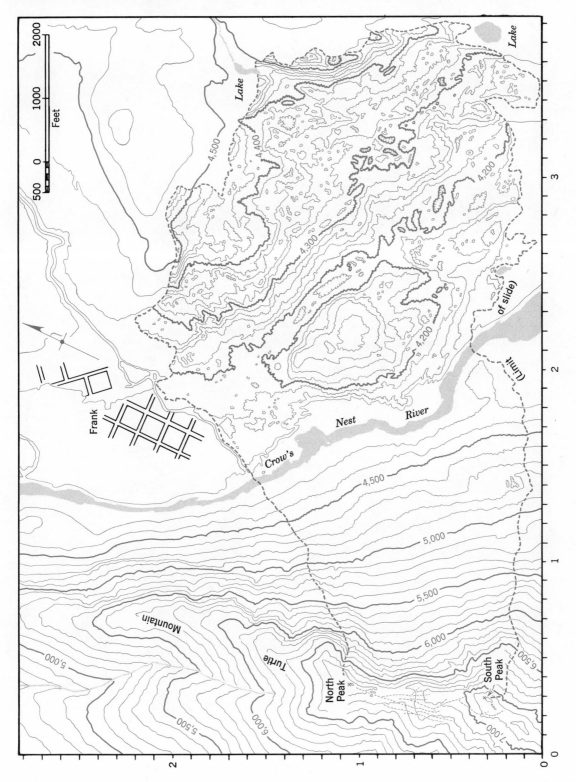

QUESTIONS

(a) What two contour intervals are used on this map?

Ans. _____ and _____ .

(b) What is the length, in miles, of the landslide area, measured from South Peak (0.3–0.3) to 3.6–1.5?

_____ yards   Ans. _____ miles

(c) What is the elevation of the hachured contour located

at 2.4–1.2?   Ans. _____ feet

At 3.3–1.4?   Ans. _____ feet

What is the summit elevation of the hill of landslide debris

at 2.2–1.0?   Ans. _____ feet

(d) Taking the volume of debris of the landslide east of the Crow's Nest River to be 30 million cubic yards, what average thickness has the landslide debris within the limits of the slide east of the river?

(To calculate the area of the slide, draw in the 500-yd grid lines, then total the area of the grid squares and part-squares included within the dashed line. For a more accurate answer, use 100-yd grid squares.)

Area of debris   _____ sq yd

Average thickness of debris _____ yd

Average thickness of debris _____ ft (Ans.)

(e) How steep is the east face of Turtle Mountain between the 6000-ft contour at 0.68–1.50 and the 5000-ft contour at 0.96–1.50? Determine the answer in feet per mile.

Vertical distance   _____ ft

Horizontal distance _____ ft   Ans. _____ ft/mi

(Continue with questions on reverse side.)

S₂

(f) Draw a triangle whose legs are scaled proportionately to the vertical and horizontal distances obtained in (e). Measure the angle of slope from this triangle with a protractor and state the answer in degrees.

(Use graph paper below)   Ans. _____°

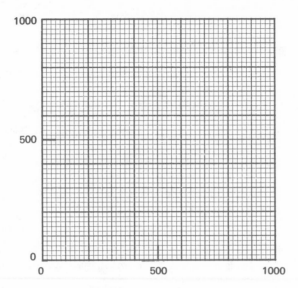

(g) Draw a profile from 0.2–0.5 to 3.7–1.5. Use a vertical scale equal to the horizontal scale of the map. Draw in the geological cross section as shown on the block diagram. Notice that the joints in the lime-stone are inclined a little less than the slope of the mountain side and are probably the planes of fracture on which the block began to slide.

(Use the blank graph paper at the bottom of page 205. Cut off the graph paper along the top line. Place the graph paper on the map so that the top edge runs along the line of profile. After the pro-file is complete, attach it here.)

Group T

STREAM FLOW AND RUNOFF

Text References

Strahler, 1969, *Physical Geography, 3rd Edition,* Chapter 25, pp. 415–427.
Strahler, 1970, *Introduction to Physical Geography, 2nd Edition,* Chapter 20, pp. 292–297.

Data table for Exercise T-2.

Little Ossipee River, Maine
(From U. S. Geological Survey)

Gauge Height (Feet)	Discharge, cfs
0.38	11
0.80	55
1.5	220
2.2	650
3.0	1400
3.8	2100
4.4	2800

Data table for Exercise T-3.

Delaware River Watershed. Port Jervis, N. Y. (3076 sq mi)
(From U. S. Geological Survey)

Rainfall	Inches
6 P.M., Sept. 28 to 6 A.M., Sept. 29:	0.1
6 A.M., Sept. 29 to 6 P.M., Sept. 29:	0.9
6 P.M., Sept. 29 to 6 P.M., Sept. 30:	3.7
6 P.M., to midnight, Sept. 30:	0.1
Total	4.8

Runoff	cfs
Sept. 28	1000 (base flow)
Sept. 29	1000 (base flow)
Sept. 30	12,000
Oct. 1	74,000
Oct. 2	47,000
Oct. 3	21,000
Oct. 4	13,000
Oct. 5	9000
Oct. 6	8000
Oct. 7	7000
Oct. 8	6000
Oct. 9	5000 (base flow)

Table of data of Exercise T-1. Wabash River, Montezuma, Indiana, March 21, 1960 (From U. S. Geological Survey)

Figures in the first column give horizontal distance from a control point on the left bank and represent the points at which the current meter was lowered. The second column gives the width of section to which the sounding applies. Notice that these widths vary because measurements are made from a bridge whose several piers prohibit uniformly spaced soundings. The fourth column gives mean velocity of each section, obtained by averaging current meter velocity readings at 0.2 and 0.8 of depth. The fifth and sixth columns give area of the section and its discharge.

1. Horizontal Distance (Feet)	2. Width of Section (Feet)	3. Depth (Feet)	4. Mean Velocity (Feet per Second)	5. Area of Section (Square Feet)	6. Discharge (cfs)
10	Left edge of water				
30	25	6.3	_____	158	171
60	30	20.8	2.50	_____	1560
90	30	27.2	3.25	816	
120	30	33.5	_____	1000	4080
150	30	37.8	4.16	_____	4700
180	23	34.8	3.52	800	
200	17	37.9	_____	644	2540
220	24	43.8	4.02	_____	4220
250	30	42.1	5.59	1260	
280	30	37.5	_____	1120	6900
310	30	38.4	5.72	_____	6580
340	30	35.5	6.34	1060	
370	29	30.3	_____	879	4220
400	27	28.9	5.11	_____	3980
430	28	23.7	3.36	664	
460	35	14.6	_____	511	552
500	45	11.8	1.24	_____	658
550	50	11.0	0.94	550	
600	52.5	11.8	_____	618	531
660	47.5	11.2	1.09	_____	580
700	45	10.0	1.34	450	
750	51	11.5	_____	586	1490
805	52.5	13.0	2.36	_____	1610
860	46.5	16.2	1.43	753	
900	45	16.7	_____	752	541
950	52	15.8	1.46	_____	1200
1005	42.5	21.8	1.98	926	
1040	35.5	15.8	_____	561	1160
1080	45	12.1	2.12	_____	1150
1130	55	6.2	1.22	341	
1190	Right edge of water				

To solve for missing numbers in table, use the following equations:

Column 4: $V = Q/A$ Divide column 6 by column 5.
Column 5: $A = Q/V$ Divide column 6 by column 4.
Column 6: $Q = AV$ Multiply column 5 by column 4.

Exercise T-1 *(continued)*   (First answer Questions (a), (b), (c), and (d) on pages 215 and 216.)

(e) Does there seem to be a significant relationship between mean velocity and depth? Describe the relationship shown by the graph. Explain in terms of the mechanics of fluid flow.

_____

_____

_____

_____

_____

_____

_____

_____

_____

_____

_____

_____

_____

_____

_____

T₁

Exercise T-1 STREAM GAUGING AND STREAM DISCHARGE

(a) Complete the table on page 213 by filling the blank spaces, following instructions accompanying the table.

(b) On the graph below, plot the stream bed profile, both at natural scale (upper plot) and 5 times vertical exaggeration (lower plot). Several points have been plotted and connected to show procedure.

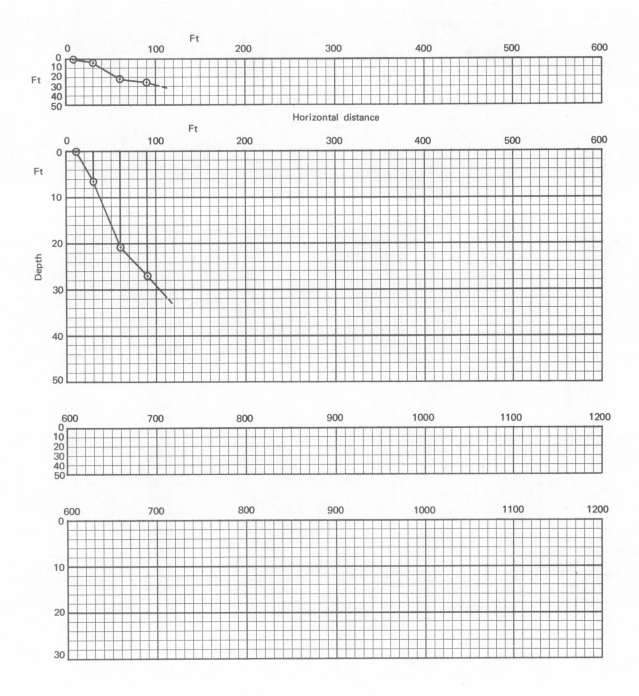

T₁

Exercise T-1 *(continued)*

(c) Sum the area and discharge columns of the table on page 213. Using these totals, compute the mean velocity of the entire stream.

Total area _____ Total discharge _____ Mean vel. _____

(d) On the graph below, plot mean velocity against depth. Enter a point for each of the 30 pairs of measurements of velocity and depth.

(Continue with question on page 214)

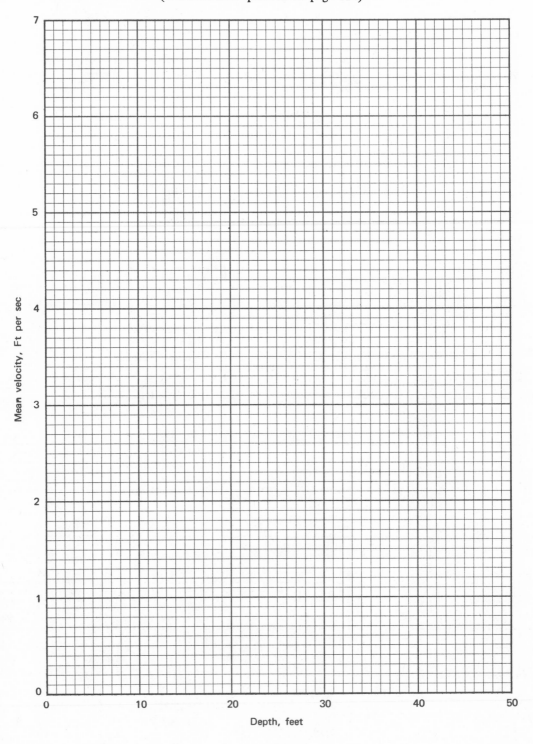

216

Exercise T-2 STAGE-DISCHARGE RATING CURVE

The table on page 211 gives observed values of gauge height (stage) and corresponding discharges for a permanent gauging station on the Little Ossipee River in Maine.

(a) Plot the data on the graph below. Fit a smooth curve to the points.

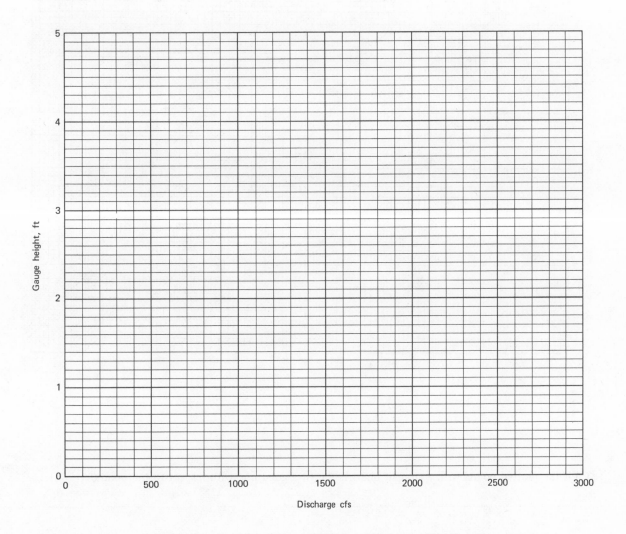

(b) Using the rating curve you have drawn, estimate discharge for the following gauge heights:

0.5 ft _____ cfs   2.6 ft _____ cfs

1.0 ft _____ cfs   4.1 ft _____ cfs

(c) Plot the same stage-discharge data on the logarithmic graph below:

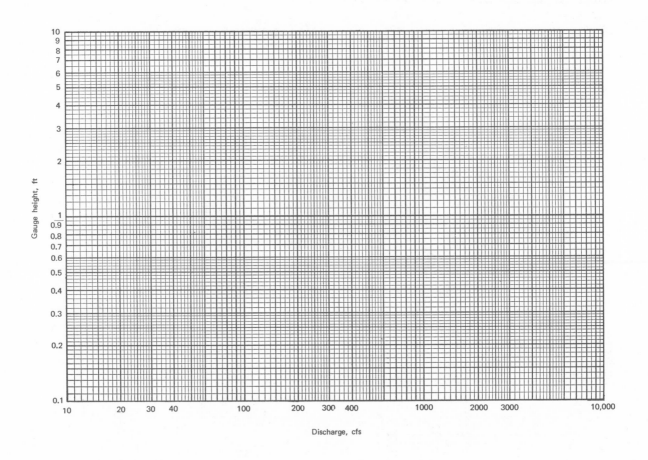

(d) Fit the plotted points with a straight line. Is the fit a good one with respect to the points?

_____

_____

(e) What is the significance of the straight-line arrangement of points on the logarithmic graph?

_____

_____

_____

(f) Which of two rating curves you have prepared (arithmetic plot vs. logarithmic plot) is easier to use for low discharges? Why?

_____

_____

Exercise T-3 PRECIPITATION AND RUNOFF

Refer to page 211 for table of precipitation and runoff of an early autumn rainstorm on the Delaware River Watershed, gauged at Port Jervis, N.Y.

(a) Plot precipitation and runoff on the graph below. Precipitation should be shown by a bar graph, using the scale on the right. Runoff should be plotted as a point centered on the calendar day. Connect the points with a smooth curve.

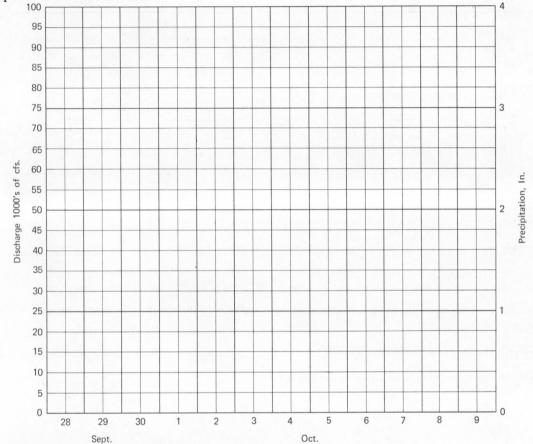

(b) Estimate the time lag for the following events:

Between onset of precipitation and onset of surface runoff: _____

Between peak precipitation and peak runoff: _____

(c) On the graph draw a smoothly rising curve of base flow from September 29 to October 9.

(d) For each day, Sept. 30 through October 8, inclusive, subtract the base flow from the daily discharge to determine the surface runoff. Multiply each day's quantity by the number of seconds in a day (86,400) to determine the daily volume of surface runoff in cubic feet. Enter data in the table below. Sum the daily volumes to obtain total storm surface runoff.

Day	Daily Discharge, cfs	Base Flow, cfs	Net Discharge, cfs	Daily Volume, cu ft
Sept. 30	_____	_____	_____	_____
Oct. 1	_____	_____	_____	_____
Oct. 2	_____	_____	_____	_____
Oct. 3	_____	_____	_____	_____
Oct. 4	_____	_____	_____	_____
Oct. 5	_____	_____	_____	_____
Oct. 6	_____	_____	_____	_____
Oct. 7	_____	_____	_____	_____
Oct. 8	_____	_____	_____	_____

Total storm volume _____ cu ft

(e) Calculate the mean depth, in feet, of the total storm volume of surface runoff. Watershed area is 3076 sq mi.

Watershed area in sq ft: $3076 \times (5280)^2 = $ _____

(Divide storm runoff volume by watershed area.)

Mean depth of storm runoff: _____ ft

Converted to depth in inches: _____ in.

(f) Compared the depth obtained in (e) with total depth of rainfall of the storm.

_____

Group U

LANDFORMS MADE BY STREAMS

Text References

Strahler, 1969, *Physical Geography, 3rd Edition*, Chapter 26, pp. 441–463.
Strahler, 1970, *Introduction to Physical Geography, 2nd Edition*, Chapter 21, pp. 308–322.

Exercise U-1 YOUNG STREAM AND GORGE (Source: Colfax, Calif., U.S. Geological Survey topographic map; scale 1:125,000)

EXPLANATORY NOTE: The American River, shown on this map, is a young stream occupying a deep, V-shaped canyon in the west slope of the Sierra Nevada range.

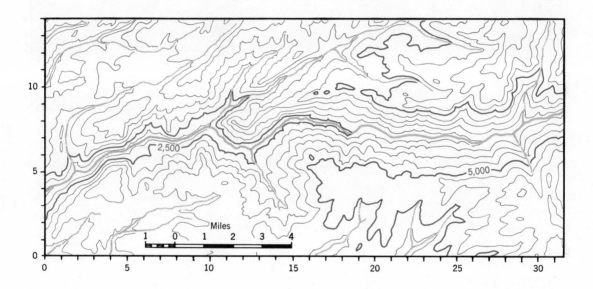

U₂

Exercise U-2 STREAM IN EARLY MATURITY (Source: St. Albans, W. Va., U.S. Geological Survey topographic map; scale 1:62,500.)

EXPLANATORY NOTE: The Kanawha River, shown on this map, has reached a stage of early maturity and has formed a flood plain between steep bluffs. (North is to the right on this map.) There is as yet insufficient width of flood plain to accommodate meanders.

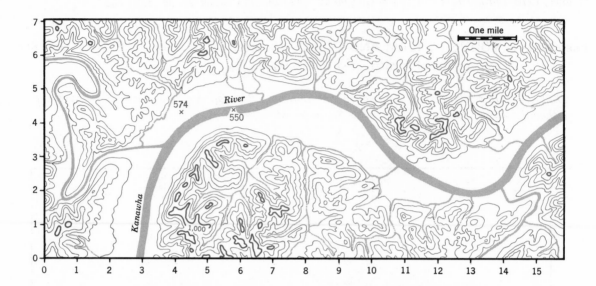

Exercise U-1 QUESTIONS (Refer to map on page 221)

(a) What contour interval is used on this map? _____ ft

(b) How deep is the canyon in the vicinity of 22-7? _____ ft

(c) What is the average gradient of the river in feet per mile? _____ ft/mi

(d) What is the gradient of the tributary stream flowing from 19-13 to 10-8? _____ ft/mi

(e) Measure the steepness of slope of the north wall of the main river canyon in the vicinity of 24-8. State in feet per mile. _____ ft/mi

(d) How many times steeper is this canyon side slope than the gradient of the river itself? _____

(e) Using the blank profile graph below, construct a profile from 24-14 to 24-0. What is the scale of this profile (inches to feet)?

Scale: 1 inch = _____ ft

What is the vertical exaggeration of the profile? _____

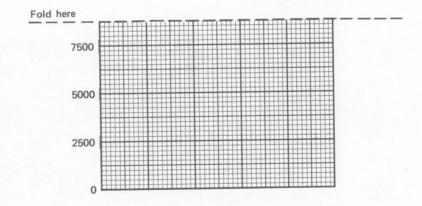

Exercise U-2 QUESTIONS (Refer to map on page 222)

(a) How wide is the river? _____ yd

(b) What is the contour interval of this map? _____ ft

(c) Estimate the elevation of the highest point shown on this map. _____ ft

(d) What is the maximum relief within the area of the map? _____ ft

(e) In what direction is the Kanahwa River flowing? Describe the evidence used in making this decision. (North is to the right.)

_____

_____

_____

_____

_____

(f) From the map alone, can the gradient of the river be determined? Explain.

_____

_____

_____

_____

_____

(g) Using the blank profile graph below, construct a profile from 7-0 to 7-7, using a vertical scale of 1000 ft equals 1 inch.

What is the vertical exaggeration of the profile? _____

Fold here

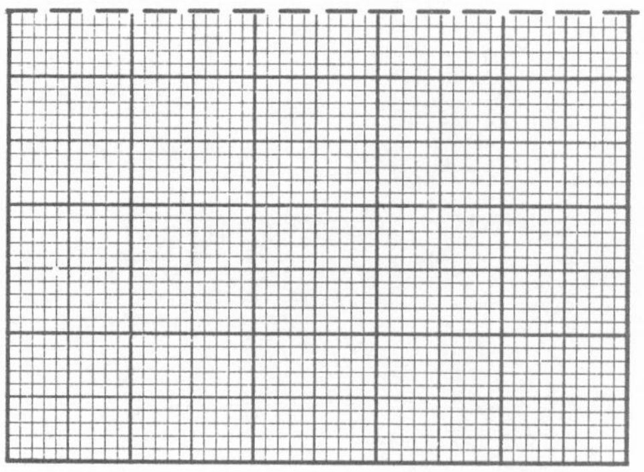

Exercise U-3 MEANDERING STREAM ON FLOOD PLAIN (Source: Gorham, Ill., U.S. Geological Survey topographic map; scale 1:24,000.)

EXPLANATORY NOTE: The Big Muddy River meander belt lies close to valley bluffs on the east. To the west extends a broad, flat alluvial plain, Oakwood Bottoms. The innermost gray band represents the river channel itself. The 350-ft contour line (dashed) reveals the existence of low natural levees bordering the channel. Three contours are omitted between 380 and 500 ft.

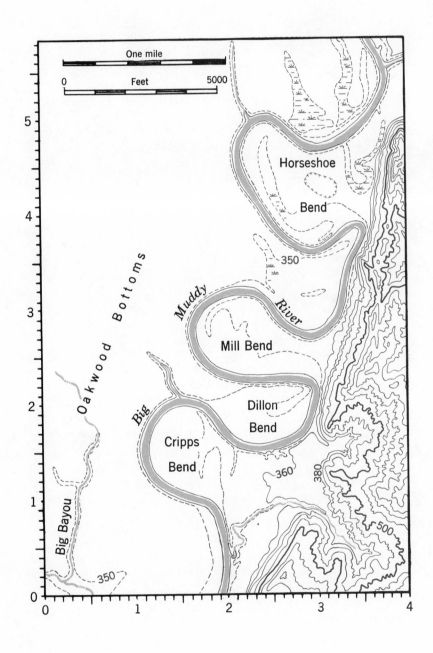

Exercise U-3 QUESTIONS

(a) What is the fractional scale (R.F.) of this map?   R.F. _____

(b) How many times greater (or smaller) is this scale than that of the map in Exercise U-2?

_____

(c) The gradient of Big Muddy River cannot be computed from this map alone. Suppose, however, that one regular contour crosses the stream at the point where the stream enters the map, while the next consecutive lower contour crosses the map at the point where the stream leaves the map. What then is the river gradient? Give in feet per mile and percent grade. Compare with the gradient of the American River, Exercise U-1.

	Big Muddy R.	American R.
Gradient, ft/mi	_____	_____
Gradient, %	_____	_____

(d) Measure *radius of meander curvature* and *channel width* for three bends of the Big Muddy River: Mill Bend, Dillon Bend, and Cripps Bend. Terms are defined as in the following diagram:

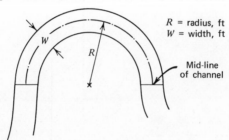

Using a pencil compass, a semicircle is fitted as nearly as possible to the mid-line of the channel to determine meander radius (*R*). Width is averaged over the semicircle to which the radius is fitted.

   Enter the three pairs of measurements in the table on page 229. Plot the pairs as three points on the blank graph below the table.

(e) In like manner, measure and plot meander radius and channel width for all of the bends shown in maps on page 228. Draw the fitted semicircles with pencil compass directly on the maps.

U3 Exercise U-3 MAPS OF MEANDER BENDS (From U.S. Geological Survey)

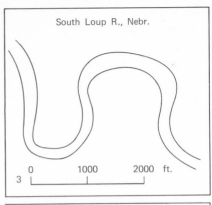

South Loup R., Nebr.

0   1000   2000 ft.

3

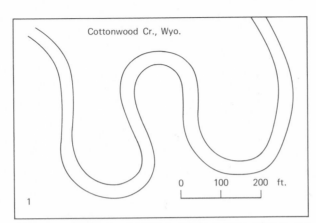

Cottonwood Cr., Wyo.

0   100   200 ft.

1

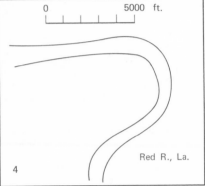

0   5000 ft.

Red R., La.

4

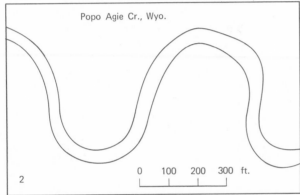

Popo Agie Cr., Wyo.

0 100 200 300 ft.

2

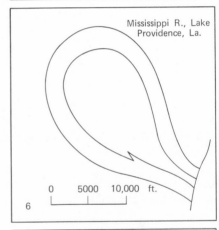

Mississippi R., Lake
Providence, La.

0 5000 10,000 ft.

6

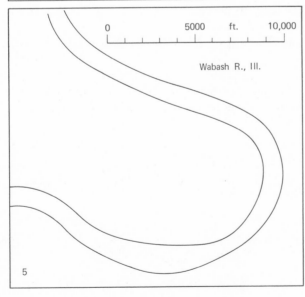

0   5000   ft.   10,000

Wabash R., Ill.

5

0   10,000   20,000 ft.

Mississippi R.,
Moss Is. Cutoff,
Ark.-Tenn.

7

228

Name_____ Date_____

Course No._____ Section_____

Exercise U-2 DATA TABLE

	R	W		R	W
Mill Bend	_____	_____	3. South Loup R. (left)	_____	_____
Dillon Bend	_____	_____	South Loup R. (right)	_____	_____
Cripps Bend	_____	_____	4. Red R.	_____	_____
1. Cottonwood Cr. (left)	_____	_____	5. Wabash R.	_____	_____
Cottonwood Cr.(center)	_____	_____	6. Miss. R., Lake Providence	_____	_____
Cottonwood Cr. (right)	_____	_____			
2. Popo Agie Cr. (left)	_____	_____	7. Miss. R., Moss Is.	_____	_____
Popo Agie Cr. (right)	_____	_____			

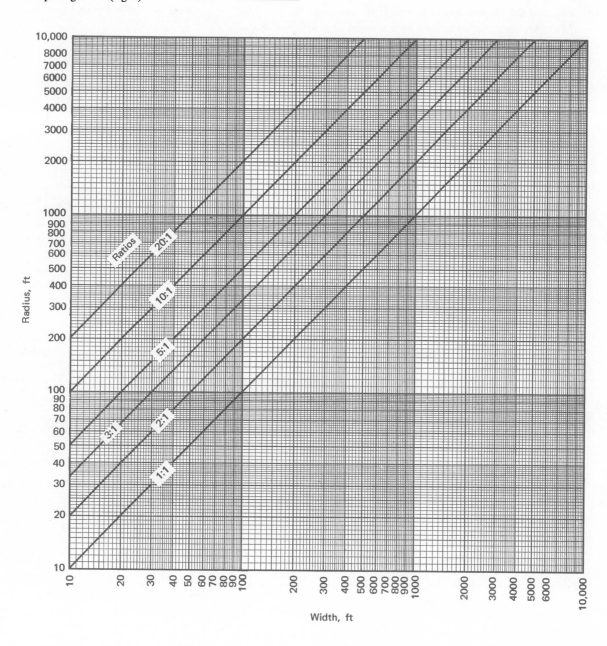

Exercise U-3 QUESTIONS *(continued)*

(f) What scales are used on the abscissa (horizontal axis) and ordinate (vertical axis) of the graph on page 229? (Give mathematical term.)

_____

(g) Notice that several parallel, slanting lines are drawn to show ratios of radius to width. What is the mathematical significance of such straight lines, sloping 45°, on this type of graph?

_____

_____

_____

_____

(h) Describe the distribution of the plotted points for the meander bends shown on the seven maps on page 228. Are they well described by a straight line with 45° slope?

_____

_____

_____

_____

(i) Estimate the best single radius-to-width ratio that can be applied to the data of all seven maps.

_____

(j) Describe the position of the three bends of Big Muddy River, on the graph, in relation to the other points. What is the average ratio for the Big Muddy? How does this ratio compare with the average estimated for the other points?

_____

_____

_____

_____

_____

_____

(k) Offer one or more hypotheses to explain why the data of Big Muddy River depart from the data of the seven maps.

_____

_____

_____

_____

_____

_____

_____

Exercise U-4 ENTRENCHED MEANDERS (Source: Rural Valley, Pa., U.S. Geological Survey topographic map; scale 1:62,500.)

EXPLANATORY NOTE: Mahoning Creek (left) and Redbank Creek (right) are entrenched meandering streams in the Appalachian Plateau Province of western central Pennsylvania. On this map north is to the right.

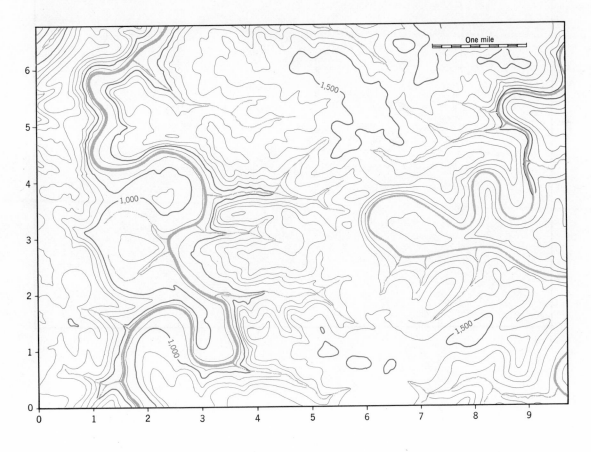

231

U₅

Exercise U-5 ALLUVIAL TERRACES

EXPLANATORY NOTE: This is a synthetic map, not representing any real area, and should be thought of as a diagram on which features are idealized. A large stream has cut down through alluvial material (with which a bedrock valley had been filled during the glacial period), leaving terraces at different levels. Curved terrace scarps are of various heights and have a radius of curvature similar to that of the meander bends of the present stream.

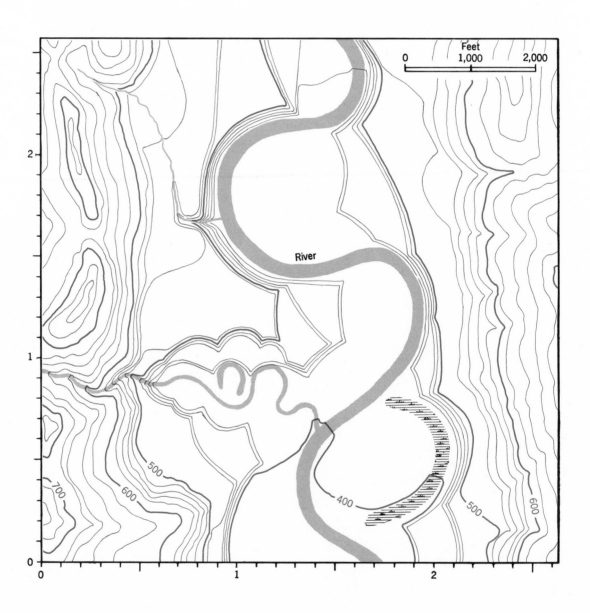

Name_____Date_____
Course No._____Section_____

U4

Exercise U-4 QUESTIONS (Refer to page 231)

(a) Give contour interval and fractional scale of the map.

C. I. _____ ft   R. F. _____

(b) Determine the maximum relief within the map area. Locate highest and lowest points by grid co-ordinates.

El. of highest point _____ ft   Grid coord. _____

El. of lowest point _____ ft   Grid coord. _____

Relief _____ ft

(c) Reproduced below is a small part of the map, showing the circular valley of an abandoned meander loop of Mahoning Creek in the vicinity of 1.7–2.8. Draw in the former course of the stream around this bend. By how many yards was the river shortened as a result of the cutoff?

Amount of shortening:

_____ yd

(d) Locate by grid coordinates, a point on either stream at which another meander cutoff may next occur.

_____

(e) How can the direction of flow of Redbank Creek be determined from the contours alone? Give direction and evidence.

_____

_____

_____

_____

(f) Study the ground slopes leading down to Mahoning Creek on meander bends in the vicinity of 2.5–1.5 and 3.5–1.5. Are slopes of equal, or unequal, steepness on opposite sides of the stream? Explain this slope configuration.

_____

_____

_____

_____

_____

_____

U5
Exercise U-5 QUESTIONS (Refer to page 232)

(a) Give contour interval and fractional scale of the map.

C. I. _____ ft   R. F. _____

(b) Determine the height of the terrace scarp at each of the following points. Give limiting values. For example, "$20 < h < 60$" means "height is greater than 20 ft but less than 60 ft."

Scarp at 1.1–2.2: _____ $< h <$ _____

Scarp at 1.6–1.7: _____ $< h <$ _____

Scarp at 1.4–1.0: _____ $< h <$ _____

(c) Measure the radius of curvature of the large stream meander bend at 1.3–1.8. (Refer to method in Exercise U-3.) Then measure the radius of curvature of the small stream meander at 1.2–0.9.

Meander at 1.3–1.8, radius _____ ft

Meander at 1.2–0.9, radius _____ ft

Of these two streams, which one cut the curved terrace scarp at 1.2–1.05?

_____

(d) What is the origin of the semicircular swamp extending from 1.7–0.2 to 1.8–0.8?

_____

_____

(e) Why does the small stream have such a steep gradient at 0.5–0.9, but such a low gradient at 0.9–0.8?

_____

_____

_____

_____

_____

(f) Why does the contour line at 1.95–1.9 bulge westward in this place instead of bending east in a sharp V as the higher contours do just east of it? What landform is present?

_____

_____

_____

_____

(g) If deep pits were to be dug in the vicinity of 1.0–1.2, what composition and texture of material would be revealed, and why?

_____

_____

_____

_____

Exercise U-6 ALLUVIAL FANS (Source: Cucamonga, Calif., U.S. Geological Survey topographic map; scale 1:62,500)

EXPLANATORY NOTE: The northern third of this map shows the southern slopes of the San Gabriel Mountain range of southern California, from which issue debris-laden streams of steep gradient. Large alluvial fans, covering the remainder of the map, have been built of gravels and bouldery debris by flood waters of these south-flowing streams. The sloping piedmont alluvial plain, therefore, consists of alluvial fans of various sizes arranged side by side. The contour interval on this map changes at the contact of the fans and mountain slopes because the difference in relief of the two types of topography is very great. This exercise makes use of field data contained in a pioneer study of alluvial fans: Rollin Eckis, The Journal of Geology, **36**, *3 (1928), 224–247.*

(The supplementary map on the reverse side of page shows the Lytle Creek alluvial fan.)

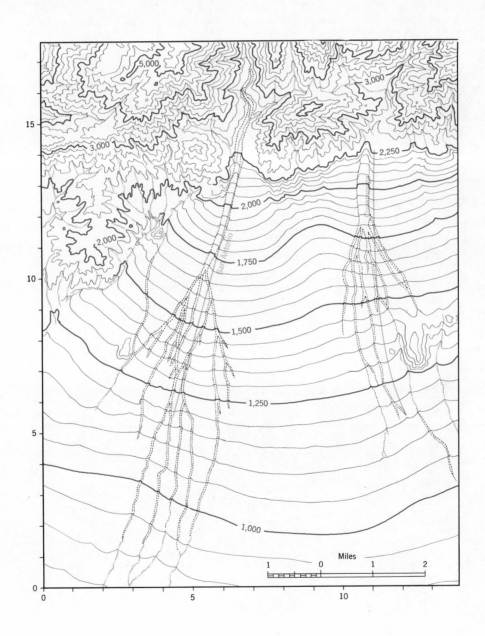

235

SAN BERNARDINO QUADRANGLE
CALIFORNIA
15 MINUTE SERIES (TOPOGRAPHIC)

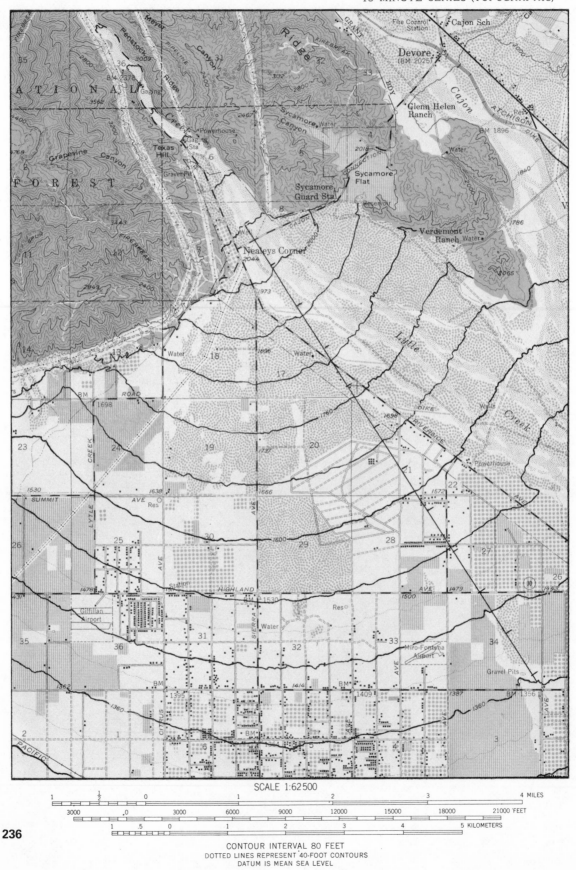

SCALE 1:62 500

CONTOUR INTERVAL 80 FEET
DOTTED LINES REPRESENT 40-FOOT CONTOURS
DATUM IS MEAN SEA LEVEL

Exercise U-6 QUESTIONS (Refer to map on page 235)

(a) Determine the contour intervals used on this map.

Mountain areas, C. I. _____ ft   Fan areas, C. I. _____ ft

(b) Stream channels (dry washes) on the fans are shown by dotted lines. How do contour lines reveal the channel boundaries and channel forms?

_____

_____

_____

(c) For San Antonio and Cucamonga fans, determine fan elevations at half-mile intervals from fan apex to fan base, 5 miles distant. Follow profile lines shown on map. Enter data in table on page 238.

(d) Determine the elevation drop within the first mile for all five fans of the table data. (Deer Canyon, Day Canyon, and Lytle Canyon are located east of the map area, in the order stated.) Enter data in spaces provided on the table. List the five fans below in order of decreasing steepness of gradient:

(Steepest (1)_____   (4)_____
gradient)
          (2)_____   (5)_____

          (3)_____   (Lowest gradient)

(e) Plot the profiles of the five fans on the blank graph on page 239. Use a different color for each profile. Label with name of canyon.

(f) Compare the profiles of the five fans. Which profile is most strongly curved; which is least?

Most strongly curved _____ Least curved _____

(g) In what way are steepness of gradient (near apex) and degree of up-concavity correlated with watershed area? (Refer to data in table.) Offer a physical explanation for the observed relationship.

_____

_____

_____

_____

_____

_____

_____

_____

_____

_____

_____

(Questions continued on page 240)

U6 Exercise U-6

Data Table — Alluvial fans of the Cucamonga Region (Data from R. Eckis and U. S. Geological Survey)

Distance, miles	San Antonio Canyon	Cucamonga Canyon	Deer Canyon	Day Canyon	Lytle Canyon
0.0	2250	2300	2750	2350	2080
0.5	————	————	2450	2120	2010
1.0	————	————	2140	1900	1935
1.5	————	————	1910	1700	1860
2.0	————	————	1680	1540	1780
2.5	————	————	1525	1430	1705
3.0	————	————	1420	1370	1640
3.5	————	————	1340	1310	1585
4.0	————	————	1280	1250	1520
4.5	————	————	1225	1205	1465
5.0	————	————	1175	1170	1415
Elevation drop in first mile:	————	————	————	————	————
Watershed area, sq mi:	26.2	10.6	3.4	4.9	47.9
Fragment size,* in. At apex:	69	90	157	112	87
At 2.5 mi:	54	30	21	19	54

*Median of lengths of 10 largest fragments in distance of 50 yd along wash.

Exercise U-6

Graph for construction of fan profiles. (Use data on page 238.)

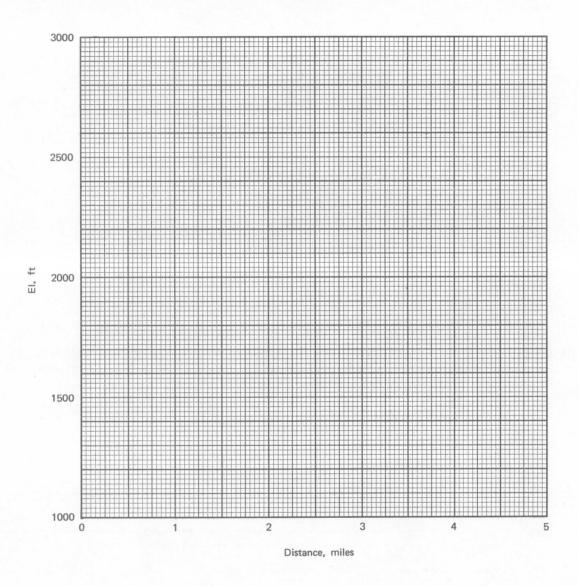

U6

(h) Study the relationship of fragment size (given in table) to both fan gradient and watershed area. Does this relationship support the explanation you have given in (g)? Discuss the correlation of fragment size with fan gradient in terms of stream transportation processes.

_____

_____

_____

_____

_____

_____

_____

_____

_____

_____

_____

_____

_____

_____

(i) Study the elevations of the fan heads at their starting points (zero distance), as given in the table. In what way are these elevations related to watershed area? Describe the observed correlation; then offer an explanation in terms of geomorphic processes.

_____

_____

_____

_____

_____

_____

_____

_____

_____

_____

_____

_____

_____

Group V

THE CYCLE OF LAND-MASS DENUDATION

Text References

Strahler, 1969, *Physical Geography, 3rd Edition*, Chapter 27, pp. 465–480.
Strahler, 1970, *Introduction to Physical Geography, 2nd Edition*, Chapter 22, pp. 324–334.

Exercise V-1 REGION IN STAGE OF YOUTH (Source: Yellowstone National Park Topographic Map, U.S. Geological Survey; scale 1:125,000)

EXPLANATORY NOTE: Much of the area of the map on page 243 represents an undulating plateau surface at 8000 to 8500 ft elevation, which may be considered as an initial land surface built by repeated outpourings of lavas. Hot springs and geysers suggest the geologic recency of volcanic activity. Low stream gradients and marshes are typical of streams flowing across the undissected upland. In strong contrast with the initial upland is the deep, youthful Grand Canyon of the Yellowstone River downstream from the Upper and Lower Falls. The oblique air photograph below is taken from Inspiration Point, just above the canyon, looking southwestward toward the falls.

U.S. Army Air Service Photograph.

Name_____Date_____
Course No._____Section_____

V 1

QUESTIONS

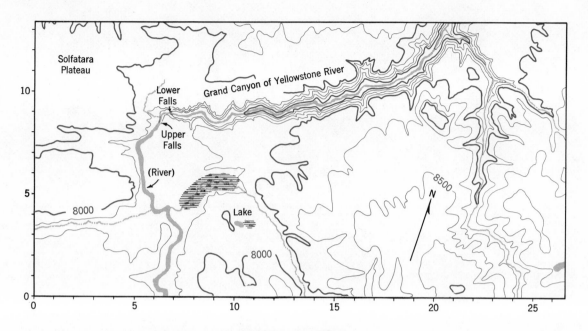

(a) Determine the contour and fractional scale of the map above.

C. I. _____ ft   R. F. _____

(b) Is the gradient of the Yellowstone River steeper or less steep below the Lower Falls than above the Upper Falls? What is the factual basis of your answer?

_____

_____

_____

_____

(c) Does the gradient of the Yellowstone, downstream from the Lower Falls, steepen, lessen, or remain constant? What is the factual basis for your answer?

_____

_____

_____

_____

(d) Refer to the air photograph on page 241. By comparison of the photograph and map, locate on the map the ground point directly beneath the airplane. Mark and label on map above.

(e) Using a blue pencil, draw all stream channels on the map that are indicated by V-indentations of contours.

V₁

(f) Determine the average angle of slope of the south wall of Yellowstone Canyon in the vicinity of 15–9 and 18–0. Measure the horizontal distance between the 7000 and 8000-ft contour lines. Plot vertical and horizontal distances to scale on the graph below and measure the slope angle with a protractor. Label angle on graph.

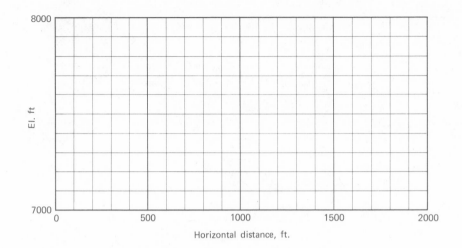

Alternate method: by trigonometry.

$$\text{Tan slope angle} = \frac{\text{vertical distance}}{\text{horizontal distance}} = \text{,}\underline{\hspace{3cm}}$$

$$\text{Arc tan } \frac{V}{H} = \underline{\hspace{3cm}}° \quad \text{(From trig tables.)}$$

(g) Is the slope angle in (f) greater than or less than the angle of repose of talus fragments? Are the talus slopes visible in the photograph steeper, or less steep, than the bare rock slopes above the talus slopes?

_____

_____

_____

_____

_____

_____

_____

_____

Exercise V-2 REGION IN STAGE OF MATURITY (Source: Belmont, N.Y., U.S. Geological
Survey topographic map; scale 1:62,500)

*EXPLANATORY NOTE: A maturely dissected region in a humid continental climate is shown without
the drainage network. All the region has been formed into closely fitting drainage basins separated by
narrow, rounded divides.*

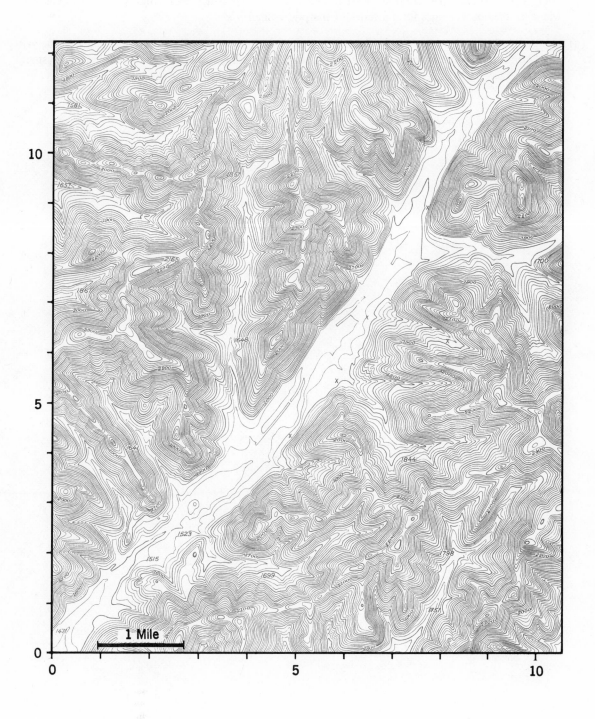

(a) Give contour interval and fractional scale of the map of page 245.

C. I. _____ R. F. _____

(b) What is the maximum relief within the map area?

Highest point _____ ft Lowest point _____ ft Relief _____ ft

(c) Using a blue pencil, draw in the drainage network for the entire map area. Indicate a stream channel wherever the contour lines form a series of sharply defined V's.

(d) Using a black pencil, outline all divides on the map. Carry the divide lines down the spurs to the valley bottoms in such a way as to enclose a single basin for each fingertip tributary of the drainage system.

EXPLANATORY NOTE: The prominent knob in the center of the map is Stone Mountain, a small intrusive body of granite surrounded by ancient gneisses and schists. Because of its greater resistance to weathering and erosion, the Stone Mountain granite formed a conspicuous monadnock while the surrounding region was reduced to a peneplain, seen now in broad, relatively flat divide areas between 950 and 1050 ft elevation. In a second erosion cycle, stream valleys were cut into the peneplain surface, producing the present topography.

Stone Mountain, on the Piedmont upland near Atlanta, Georgia, is a striking monadnock about 1.5 mi (2.4 km) long and rising 650 ft (193 m) above the surrounding Piedmont peneplain surface. The rock is a light-gray granite, almost entirely free of joints, and has been rounded into a smooth dome by weathering processes. (Photograph by U.S. Army Air Service.)

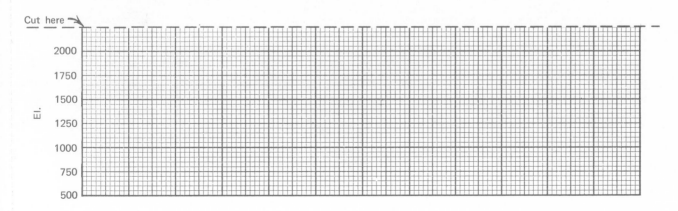

Exercise V-3 *(continued)*

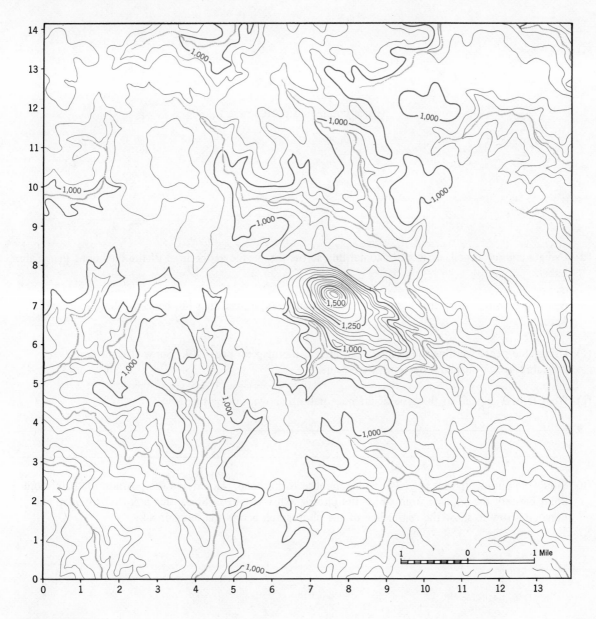

QUESTIONS

(a) Give the contour interval used on the map above.

C. I. _____ ft

(b) How high does the summit of Stone Mountain rise above the peneplain surface 1 mile west of the summit?

_____ ft

V

3

(c) Construct a topographic profile through the summit of Stone Mountain from 0.5–1.5 to 12–11. Use the blank graph on page 247. Cut the graph along the line indicated and apply it directly to the map. When the profile is complete, paste it in the space below.

(Place completed profile here.)

(d) Using a colored pencil, draw a horizontal line across the profile at the level of the Piedmont peneplain. Label.

(e) Below the profile, draw the outlines of the resistant granite mass that lies beneath Stone Mountain. Label.

(f) Using blue pencil, outline the drainage pattern on the map on page 249. Show streams wherever indicated by a V-shaped inflection of contours.

(g) What term is applied to the type of drainage pattern shown on the map?

_____

_____

(h) Study the photograph on page 247 with reference to the map. Determine the position of the ground point beneath the airplane from which the photograph was taken. Show this point on the map and draw an arrow to show the center line of the photograph across the monadnock.

Exercise V-4 MOUNTAINOUS DESERT LANDSCAPE (Source: Avawatz Mountains, Calif., U.S. Geological Survey topographic map: scale 1:250,000)

EXPLANATORY NOTE: This map shows a portion of the Basin and Range physiographic province, the region used by Professor W. M. Davis to typify the land-mass denudation cycle in an arid climate. Death Valley, a downfaulted block, lies well below sea level despite filling with vast quantities of alluvium swept down from the Amargosa and Panamint Ranges, upfaulted blocks which bound the valley on either side. The air photograph is taken from a point above Death Valley, looking southeastward up the Amargosa River. Owl Lake and Lost Lake are ephemeral playa lakes occupying independent closed depressions considerably higher than Death Valley.

Copyrighted Spence Air Photos.

Exercise V-4 *(continued)*

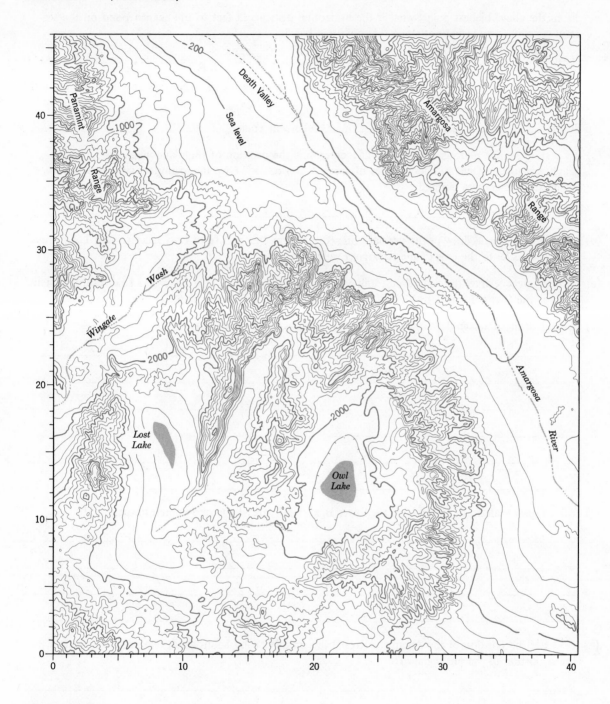

QUESTIONS

(a) Give the contour interval used on the map above.

C. I. _____

Calculate the number of square miles covered by the map.

_____ sq mi

(Continue on reverse side of page.)

(b) Locate the highest point of the Amargosa Range lying within the map area. Estimate its elevation and give grid coordinates.

El. _____ ft   Grid coordinates _____

From the above highest point, what is the horizontal distance in feet to the nearest point on the sea-level contour (zero elevation) along the mountain base?

_____ ft

Calculate the ratio of vertical drop to horizontal distance along the line specified above. State the ratio in percent of grade.

Ratio _____   Percent grade _____

(c) By a study of the photograph on page 251 determine the position of the plane when the air photograph was taken. Give grid coordinates of the position below. Give the azimuth of the line along which the camera was pointed.

Grid coordinates _____   Azimuth _____

(d) Using a blue pencil, draw in the drainage line (dry stream channel) from Lost Lake to Owl Lake, then from Owl Lake to the axis of the Amargosa valley.

(e) In black pencil, draw the watershed (drainage divide) for the entire Lost Lake-Owl Lake runoff system. Start at the Owl Lake outlet at 25–20. (Part of the basin lies off the map).

(f) Predict future drainage developments affecting Owl Lake and Lost Lake.

_____

_____

_____

_____

_____

_____

(g) What type of landform is shown in the lower right-hand part of the photograph on page 251?

_____

_____

_____

_____

(h) How has the position of the Amargosa River been influenced by landform development (as seen in the lower portion of the photograph)?

_____

_____

_____

_____

_____

_____

Group W

QUANTITATIVE ANALYSIS OF EROSIONAL LANDFORMS

W

Text References

Strahler, 1969, *Physical Geography, 3rd Edition,* Chapter 28, pp. 481–500.
Strahler, 1970, *Introduction to Physical Geography, 2nd Edition,* Chapter 22, pp. 328–331.

Stream Orders (Use in Exercise W-1)

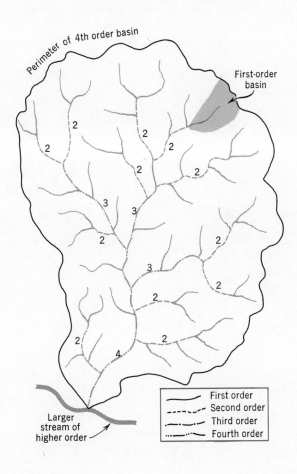

Graph for Exercise W-1 (Instructions on page 259)

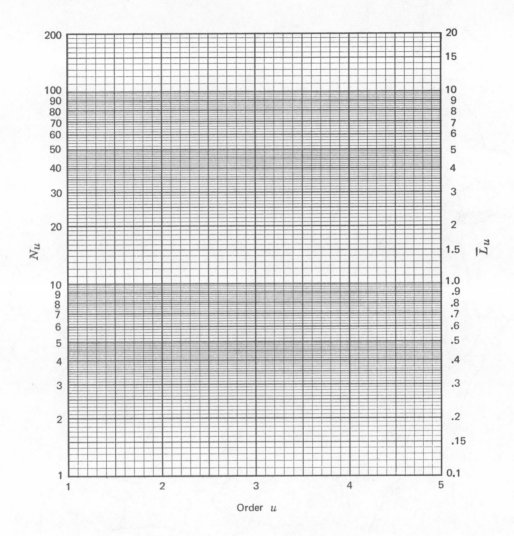

Order *u*

W₁

Stream Net for Exercise W-1

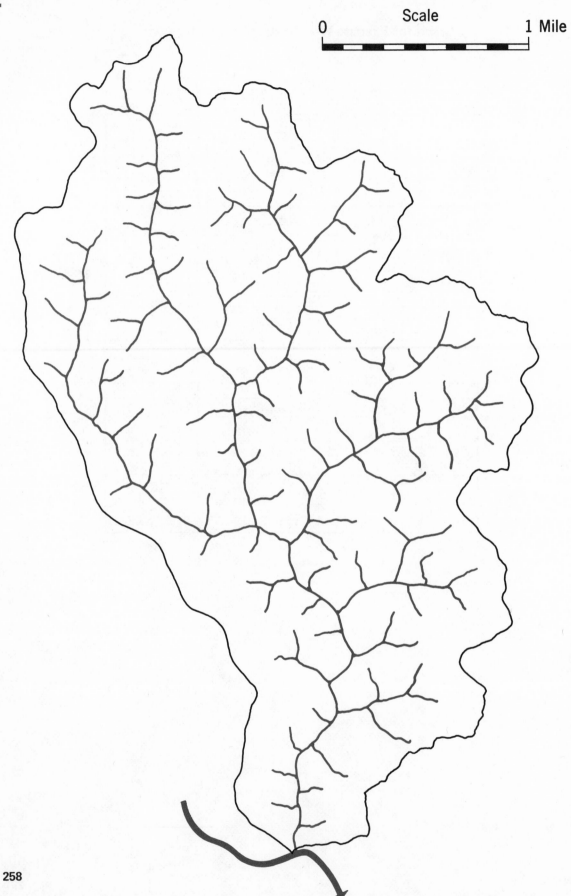

Exercise W-1 STREAM ORDERS, NUMBERS, AND LENGTHS

The map on page 258 shows a stream net and perimeter of a drainage basin. The map is a composite of actual drainage basin elements in the Appalachian Plateau region of Kentucky. The region is in the mature stage of the cycle of land-mass denudation. The drainage pattern is of a pure dendritic type and is characteristic of regions of horizontal sedimentary strata.

(a) Assign orders to all segments of the stream system. Select several pencils of different colors and assign a color to each order. Find and mark in color all first-order segments. Then find and mark in color the second-order segments; followed by the third, and so forth. Prepare a key to your color code. Refer to the ordered stream net on page 255 as a guide.

(b) Count the numbers of segments of each order. Check your count at least twice. Record the data in the table below. Determine bifurcation ratios between successive orders and record in the table.

Stream Order u	No. of Segments N_u	Bifurcation Ratio R_b
1	_____	
		_____
2	_____	
		_____
3	_____	
		_____
4	_____	

(c) Plot the numbers of segments of each order on the blank graph on page 257. Fit the points with a straight line. Label.

(d) Is the straight line a good description of the arrangement of points on the graph? Evaluate in terms of degree of conformity to Horton's law of stream numbers.

_____

_____

_____

_____

_____

_____

W

1 Exercise W-1 *(continued)*

(e) Using a map measurer, measure the total length of first-order stream segments on the map on page 258. Measure total lengths of segments of each of the remaining orders. Enter data in the table below. Convert total lengths into miles. (See scale on map.)

Stream Order u	No. of Segments N_u	Total length of streams of order, u. Inches ΣL_u	Total length, miles ΣL_u	Mean Length of segments, Miles $\overline{L}_u$	Cumulative Mean Length Miles $\overline{L}_u$	Length Ratio R_L
1	_____	_____	_____	_____	_____	
2	_____	_____	_____	_____	_____	_____
3	_____	_____	_____	_____	_____	_____
4	_____	_____	_____	_____	_____	_____

(f) Divide total length (miles) of each order by the number of stream segments of that order, obtaining mean length of segments. Enter data in table above.

(g) Calculate cumulative mean length for each order and enter in the table above.

(h) Calculate length ratio for each pair of successive orders. Enter ratios in table above.

(i) Plot the cumulative stream length data on the graph on page 257, using the scale on the right-hand side of the graph. Fit the points with a straight line. Label.

(j) Comment on the degree to which the length data conform to Horton's law of stream lengths.

_____
_____
_____
_____
_____
_____

Exercise W-2 BASIN AREA AND DRAINAGE DENSITY

(a) Using a *polar planimeter,* measure the area of the drainage basin outlined on page 258. If no polar planimeter is available, estimate the area by counting squares of a sheet of graph paper placed over the map. Convert the data from square inches to square miles, and enter below:

Basin area, sq in _____   Basin area, sq mi _____

(b) Calculate the drainage density of the entire basin. (Divide total stream length, in miles, by basin area, in square miles.)

Total stream length   _____ mi

Basin area   _____ sq mi

Drainage density:

_____ mi/sq mi

(c) Comment upon the measured drainage density of this area in comparison with the known range of drainage density values in natural fluvial systems.

_____

_____

_____

_____

_____

_____

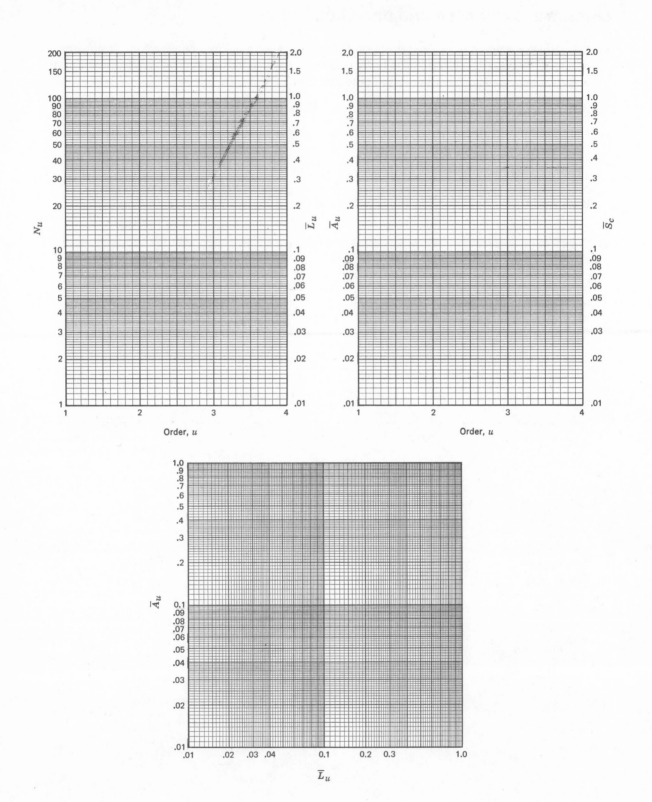

Exercise W-3 HORTON'S LAWS

The accompanying tables give morphometric data for Little Mill Creek, Ohio, a basin of the fourth order with an area of 2.7 sq mi (data from M. E. Morisawa, 1959). The fourth-order basin is not complete, hence values in parentheses should not be plotted. The data can be regarded as a combined sample consisting of five complete third-order basins.

Order	Number of Streams	Bifurcation Ratio	Mean stream length, mi.	Cumulative Mean Stream Length, mi.	Length Ratio
u	N_u	R_b	$\bar{L}_u$	$\bar{L}_u$	R_L
1	104		0.07	_____	
2	22	_____	0.19	_____	_____
3	5	_____	0.65	_____	_____
4	1		(1.2)		

(a) In the above table, compute and enter bifurcation ratios between orders 1 and 2, and between orders 2 and 3. Compute a mean bifurcation ratio, using the two ratios in the table.

$$\text{Mean } R_b \text{ _____}$$

(b) Plot the data of numbers and orders on the blank graph on page 262. Fit the points with a straight line. (Plot only orders 1, 2, and 3.)

(c) Enter cumulative lengths in the table above. Compute length ratios from the cumulative data for orders 1 and 2, and for orders 2 and 3. Enter in the table above.

(d) Plot the cumulative length data on the graph on page 262. Fit the points with a straight line.

(e) Evaluate the plotted data of stream orders and stream lengths? To what degree do the data conform to Horton's laws of stream numbers and stream lengths? Is the sample adequate in size to sustain such an evaluation?

_____

_____

_____

_____

_____

_____

_____

_____

Order u	Mean Basin Area, sq mi $\bar{A}_u$	Area Ratio R_A	Mean Channel Slope, % $\bar{S}_c$	Slope Ratio R_s
1	0.025		0.37	
2	0.12	_____	0.12	_____
3	0.58	_____	0.04	_____
4	(2.7)		(0.01)	

(f) Using data for Little Mill Creek in the table above, compute the area ratios between orders 1 and 2 and between orders 2 and 3. Enter in the table.

(g) Plot the mean basin area data for orders 1, 2, and 3, on the blank graph on page 262. Fit the points with a straight line. Label.

(h) Compute the slope ratios between orders 1 and 2 and between orders 2 and 3. Enter in the table above.

(i) Plot the mean channel slope for orders 1, 2, and 3 on the graph on page 262. Fit the points with a straight line. Label.

(j) Evaluate the plotted data of basin area and channel slope in terms of the degree to which they conform to Horton's laws of basin areas and stream slopes.

_____

_____

_____

_____

_____

_____

(k) On the double-logarithmic graph on page 262, plot the mean basin areas against mean stream lengths (cumulative) for orders 1, 2, and 3. Fit the points with a straight line.

(l) Evaluate the results in (k) in terms of agreement with the law of allometric growth.

_____

_____

_____

_____

_____

_____

_____

_____

LANDFORMS MADE BY GLACIERS

Text References

Strahler, 1969, *Physical Geography, 3rd Edition*, Chapter 29, pp. 501–524.
Strahler, 1970, *Introduction to Physical Geography, 2nd Edition*, Chapter 23, pp. 336–352.

Exercise X-1 YOUNG STAGE OF ALPINE GLACIATION (Source: Cloud Peak, Wyo., U.S. Geological Survey topographic map: scale 1:125,000)

EXPLANATORY NOTE: Steep-walled cirques have been cut into the broadly rounded summit of the Big Horn range in northern Wyoming, but much of the preglacial surface remains. The cirques contain lakes which form chainlike groups extending down the glacial troughs which lead from the cirques.

Block Diagram of Map Area (By E. Raisz)

Exercise X-2 MATURE STAGE OF ALPINE GLACIATION (Source: Hayden Peak, Utah, U.S. Geological Survey topographic map: scale 1:125,000)

EXPLANATORY NOTE: The map and block diagram show a maturely glaciated portion of the great Uinta Mountain range of northern Utah. North is toward the right. Broad, relatively flat-floored cirques are separated by narrow, steep-walled divides, consisting of pointed horns connected by sharp aretes. Streams have cut deep V-shaped canyons into the cirque mouths.

Block Diagram of Map Area

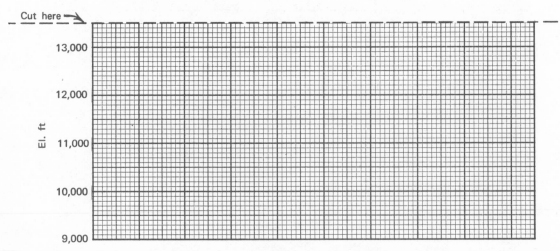

Exercise X-1 QUESTIONS

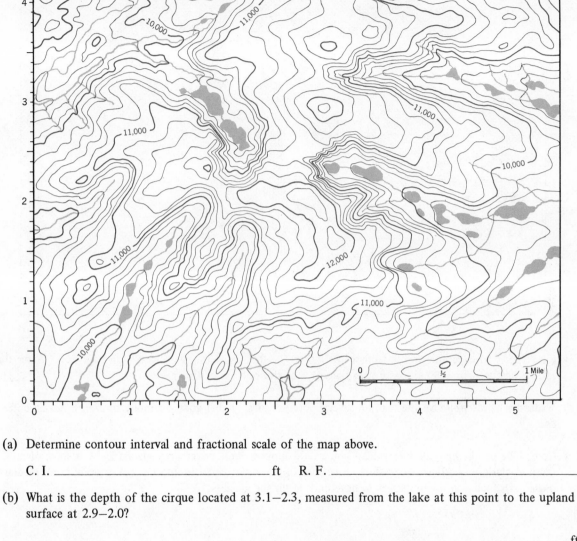

(a) Determine contour interval and fractional scale of the map above.

   C. I. _____ ft   R. F. _____

(b) What is the depth of the cirque located at 3.1–2.3, measured from the lake at this point to the upland surface at 2.9–2.0?

   _____ ft

(c) Using black pencil, outline the main divide of the mountain range. Explain why cirques heading on the east side of the range have eaten back closer to the main divide than those heading on the west side of the range.

   _____

   _____

   _____

   _____

   _____

   _____

(d) Using color pencil, lay out on the map the shortest possible route for a trail across the range from 5.5–2.3 to 0.0–1.5 in such a way that the gradient nowhere exceeds 1600 ft per mi. Avoid all cirques and troughs.

267

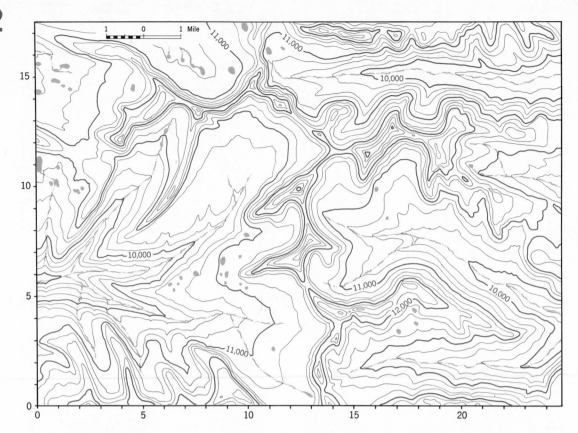

(a) Construct a topographic profile from 14.0-17.5 to 2.0-0.0, using the blank graph on page 266. After the profile has been completed, paste it in the space at the bottom of this page.

(b) Write the word *cirque* on the map on several good cirques. Label good examples of *arêtes, horns,* and *cols.*

(c) Color blue on the map all areas which you would suppose were covered by glacial ice at a stage of maximum glaciation. Add arrows to show directions of ice movement. In another color, draw in all medial moraines which you might expect to have existed on the glaciers.

(Attach completed profile here)

Exercise X-3 MORAINE AND PITTED OUTWASH PLAIN (Source: St. Croix Dalles, Wis.-Minn., U.S. Geological Survey topographic map: scale 1:62,500)

EXPLANATORY NOTE: Running across this map from northeast to southwest is a terminal moraine belt composed of innumerable small hills and depressions. To the southeast of this moraine is a sloping outwash plain containing ice-block lakes. North of the moraine is a lower area with marshes and drumlins, which was beneath the ice and has a cover of thin ground moraine.

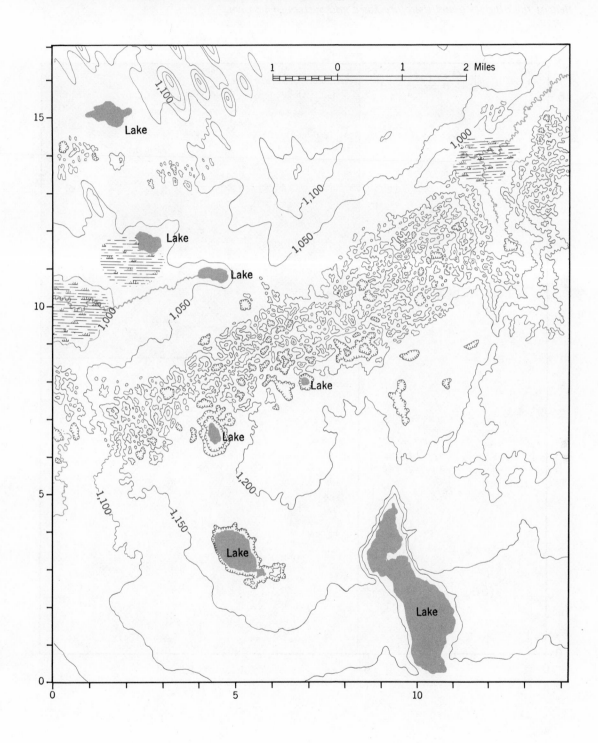

Exercise X-4 ESKER AND DRUMLINS (Source: Map A, Passadumkeag, Maine, 1:62,500. Map B, Hull, Mass., 1:31,680, Map C, Weedsport N.Y., 1:62,500 U.S. Geological Survey topographic maps)

EXPLANATORY NOTE: Map A shows an esker ridge, named Enfield Horseback, running from north to south down the center of the map. Maps B and C show drumlins from two well-known drumlin localities, Boston Bay and western New York State, respectively. Note that the scale of Map B differs from that of the other two and therefore has a grid system of its own.

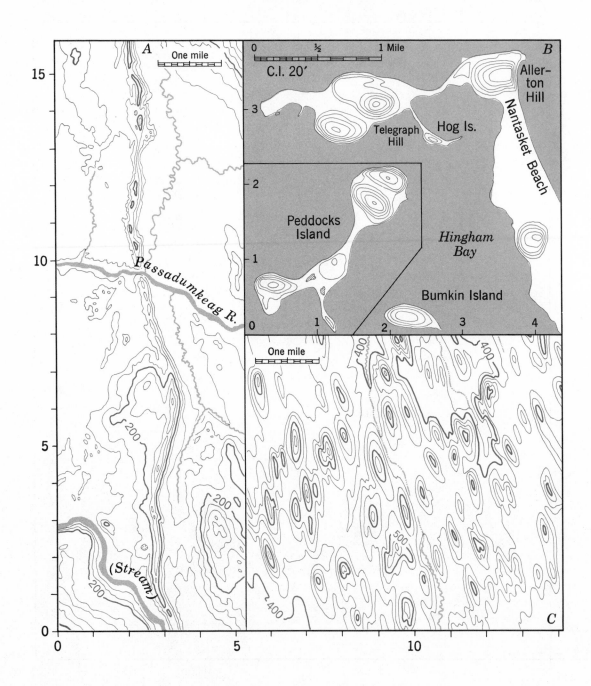

Name_____Date_____
Course No._____Section_____

X₃

Exercise X-3 QUESTIONS (Refer to map on page 269)

(a) Give contour interval and fractional scale used on the map.

   C. I. _____   R. F. _____

(b) How wide is the terminal moraine belt in the center of the map?

   _____ mi

(c) How deep is the closed depression at 8.5—8.8? Give limiting depths with respect to the lowest outlet point.

   _____

(d) What is the elevation of the surface of the lake at 4.5—6.5?

   _____

(e) Calculate the slope, in feet per mile, of the outwash plain surface between 6.0—7.5 and 9.0—0.0.

   _____ ft/mi

(f) Give the compass bearing or azimuth on which the ice was moving, as indicated by the orientation of the drumlins at 4.0—16.0 and by the trend of the moraine belt.

   _____

(g) Did the ice advance over the area now covered by the outwash plain? What is the evidence?

   _____

   _____

   _____

   _____

   _____

(h) Explain why the ground surface north of the moraine belt (elevation 1000 to 1050 ft) is lower than the surface of the outwash plain south of the moraine belt (elevation 1200 to 1250).

   _____

   _____

   _____

   _____

   _____

   _____

₄ **Exercise X-4 QUESTIONS** (Refer to map on page 270)

Map A

(a) How many yards wide is this esker, approximately?

_____ yd

(b) How high is the esker crest above the surrounding lowland, just north of the Passadumkeag River?

_____ ft

(c) Why does the esker crest rise and fall in elevation?

_____

_____

(d) Explain the closed depressions at 2.3−13.9.

_____

_____

Map B

(e) Give the length, width, and height of four drumlins on the map, locating each by grid coordinates.

	1	2	3	4
Length, ft	_____	_____	_____	_____
Width, ft	_____	_____	_____	_____
Height	_____	_____	_____	_____
Grid coord.	_____	_____	_____	_____

Map C

(f) How many drumlins are shown on this map? Count all hills represented by one or more closed contours.

_____

(g) Which drumlins are higher, those on Map C or those on Map B? Compare the highest three on each map.

Map C   _____   _____   _____

Map B   _____   _____   _____

(h) Estimate the azimuth of ice movement during the formation of the drumlins on Maps B and C.

Map B _____   Map C _____

(i) Drumlins of Map B are somewhat differently shaped than those on Map C. Describe and explain this difference.

_____

_____

_____

Group Y

LANDFORMS MADE BY WAVES AND CURRENTS

Text References

Strahler, 1969, *Physical Geography*, 3rd Edition, Chapter 30, pp. 525–547.
Strahler, 1970, *Introduction to Physical Geography*, 2nd Edition, Chapter 24, pp. 354–370.

EXPLANATORY NOTES

EXERCISE Y-1: Shoreline of Submergence, Stage of Early Youth. *(Source: Brest, France, topographic sheet No. 21; scale 1:200,000)*

The coastal region around the port of Brest lies in the peninsula of Brittany, which projects westward into the Atlantic Ocean. The coast here is deeply embayed and represents a shoreline of submergence modified appreciably by wave erosion only where the shore is exposed to waves of the open sea. This coastline resembles in many ways the Maine coast of the United States, but lies much farther north (48°N) and was never modified by intensive glacial action, as was the Maine coast. Submarine contours are shown as dashed lines for depths of 1, 5, 10, 20, 30, 40, and 50 meters. Contour interval on land is 20 meters.

EXERCISE Y-2: Young Shoreline of Submergence with Bars. *(Source: Wellington, Ont., topographic maps; scale 1:63,360. Geological Survey of Canada)*

The north shore of Lake Ontario is a shoreline of submergence on a topography developed first by normal stream erosion and associated weathering and mass wasting processes, then heavily glaciated by the Pleistocene ice sheets. A baymouth bar separates Yeo Lake from Wellington Bay, and a midbay bar has cut off the inner part of Athol Bay to produce Spence Lake.

EXERCISE Y-3: Barrier Island Shoreline. *(Source: Accomac, Va., U.S. Geological Survey, topographic map; scale 1:62,500)*

A barrier island represented by Metomkin Island and Cedar Island is separated from the mainland by a lagoonal belt consisting of expanses of open water, Metomkin Bay and Floyd's Bay, and of salt marsh with sinuous tidal creeks. At some stage prior to the appearance of the barrier island, the shoreline lay just east of the 10-ft contour line on the seaward side of Parker Neck, Bailey Neck, Joynes Neck, and Custis Neck. The age of this earlier shoreline is difficult to determine.

273

EXERCISE Y-4: Sandy Hook Split. *(Source: Navesink, N.J., topographic map: scale 1:24,000, State of New Jersey, Department of Conservation and Development)*

    Sandy Hook is a large spit extending north from Navesink Highlands into the Atlantic Ocean and forming a part of the enclosure of Lower Bay of New York Harbor. It is formed, in part, of sand carried northward along the New Jersey coast by shore drifting processes. Numerous beach ridges show various stages in the growth of the spit. The tendency of these ridges to recurve westward or landward is typical of complex spits. The tip of the spit is said to have grown about one mile since 1764, one-half mile since 1865.

EXERCISE Y-5: Elevated Shorelines and Beach Ridges. *(Source: Berea, Ohio, U.S. Geological Survey topographic map: scale 1:62,500)*

    Lake Erie, whose present shoreline is located in the northern part of this map, formerly stood higher than at present. Three ridges mark previous higher stands of the water level; Butternut Ridge, the highest, is also the oldest; Middle Ridge and North Ridge mark progressively lower stages. On both Middle Ridge and Butternut Ridge, a well-developed beach ridge is indicated by the contours, whereas North Ridge is simply a low, wave-cut escarpment. The present shoreline of Lake Erie is a good example of a mature shoreline with a continuous wave-cut scarp and numerous hanging valleys.

Profile graph for Exercise Y-5.

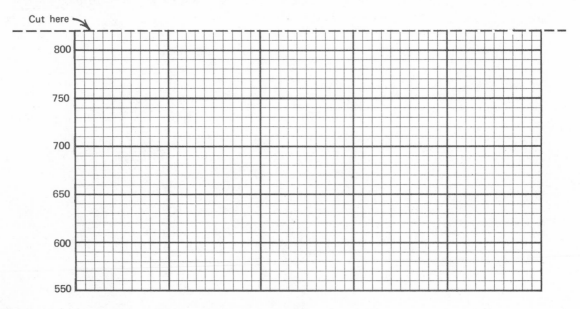

Exercise Y-1 SHORELINE OF SUBMERGENCE, STAGE OF YOUTH

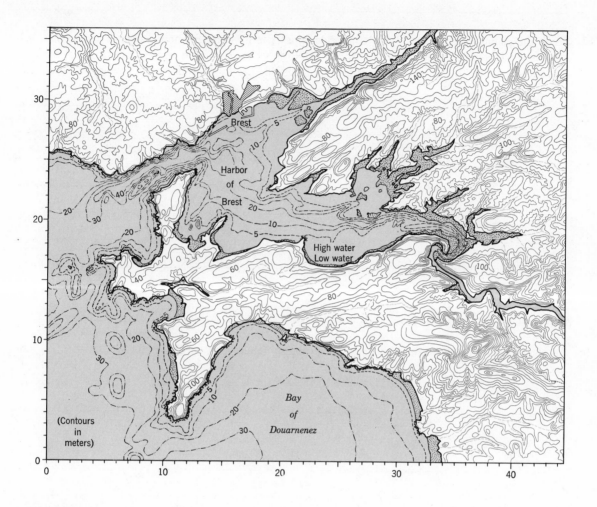

QUESTIONS

Read the explanatory note on page 273.

(a) In red pencil, mark on the map above all parts of the shoreline where a marine cliff is well developed. In blue pencil, shade all probable sand or shingle beaches.

(b) Draw lines in black pencil on the map to give a reconstruction of the drowned-stream system, which may have occupied the Harbor of Brest before the region was submerged. Carry the same lines inland up the stream valleys.

Y₁

(c) Why are there few prominent cliffs along the shoreline of the Harbor of Brest?

_____

_____

_____

(d) Study the peninsula ending at 11-4. Which side appears to have undergone the greater marine erosion? What is the topographic evidence? Is this configuration what you would expect, knowing that the open Atlantic Ocean lies to the west, whereas a bay 15 mi wide lies to the southeast? Discuss this problem.

_____

_____

_____

_____

_____

_____

_____

_____

(e) To what stage of development would you assign the shoreline between 25-22 and 31-21?

_____

_____

Between 22-10 and 34-0?

_____

_____

(f) The stippled zone bordering the shore lies between mean low water line and mean high water, and is thus alternately exposed and covered by the tide. In the bay heads near 30-20, what type of deposit does the stippled zone represent?

_____

_____

_____

276

Exercise Y-2 YOUNG SHORELINE OF SUBMERGENCE WITH BARS

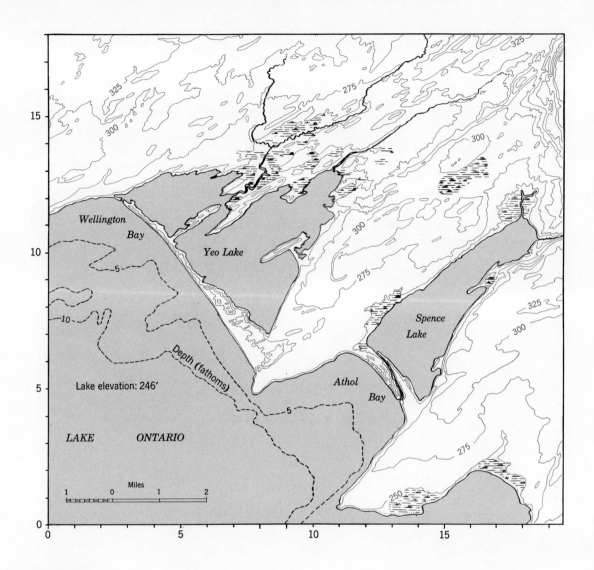

QUESTIONS

Read the explanatory note on page 273.

(a) What is the height (feet) above lake level of the small hills at 6.8–8.0?

_____ ft

(b) Is it likely that these hills are sand dunes, or that they are beach-ridge deposits thrown up by storm waves? Explain.

_____

_____

_____

_____

Y 2

(c) What is peculiar about the form of the outlet channel through the bar between Spence Lake and Athol Bay? Explain in terms of the beach drifting process. Are tidal currents responsible for keeping this channel clear?

_____

_____

_____

_____

_____

_____

(d) Using a color pencil, redraw the shoreline as a smooth, simple shoreline of early maturity passing approximately through 0.0–14.0, 6.0–11.0, 10.0–8.0, 16.0–4.0, and 19.0–0.0. Imagine all headlands to be cut back to this line. In black pencil redraw the contours to show the cliffed headlands and baymouth bars. Add baymouth bars where appropriate.

Exercise Y-3 BARRIER ISLAND SHORELINE

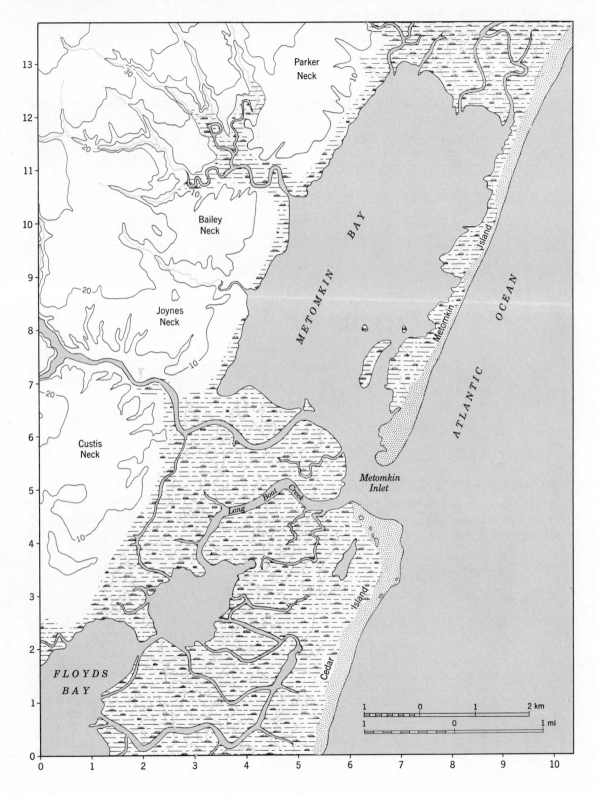

(Questions on reverse side of page)

Y3

Exercise Y-3 QUESTIONS

Read explanatory note on page 273.

(a) How far seaward of the earlier shoreline does the barrier island shoreline lie in the vicinity of the northern end of Metomkin Bay?

_____ mi

In the vicinity of Cedar Island?

_____ mi

(b) Why does the distance measured in (a) increase toward the south? Give two possible explanations.

_____

_____

_____

_____

_____

_____

(c) Why are the ends of Cedar Island Metomkin Island offset (out of alignment) at Metomkin Inlet? Explain in terms of shore drifting processes.

_____

_____

_____

_____

(d) Tide marsh and tidal streams extend inland into the valleys between Parker Neck and Bailey Neck, and between Custis Neck and Joynes Neck. How can these features be explained in terms of glacial changes of sea level and associated activities of stream erosion and tidal deposition? Reconstruct the events in chronological order.

_____

_____

_____

_____

_____

_____

_____

Name_____Date_____   Y4

Course No._____Section_____

Exercise Y-4 SANDY HOOK SPIT

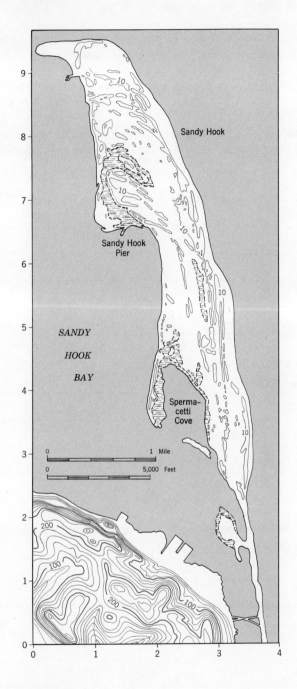

Read the explanatory note on page 274.

(Questions on reverse side of page)

Y4

Exercise Y-4 QUESTIONS

(a) What contour interval is used on the spit?   C.I. _____ ft

What contour interval is used on the mainland?   C.I. _____ ft

(b) Using a color pencil, sketch a series of curved lines to show a succession of beach ridges produced during the formation of the spit. Be guided by the contour patterns.

(c) Draw numerous short arrows close to the shoreline to show direction of dominant beach drift on both sides of the spit.

(d) Using a color pencil, different from that used in (b), color at least three areas in which you might expect to find sand dunes resting upon beach deposits. Study the contours closely for indications of dune forms.

(e) What is the origin of the marsh in the vicinity of 1.4—7.6?

_____

_____

_____

_____

_____

(f) What is the origin of Spermacetti Cove?

_____

_____

_____

_____

_____

(g) Do the Navesink Highlands (mainland) show any topographic forms produced by wave erosion? If so, describe and locate the forms.

_____

_____

_____

_____

_____

_____

Exercise Y-5 ELEVATED SHORELINES AND BEACH RIDGES

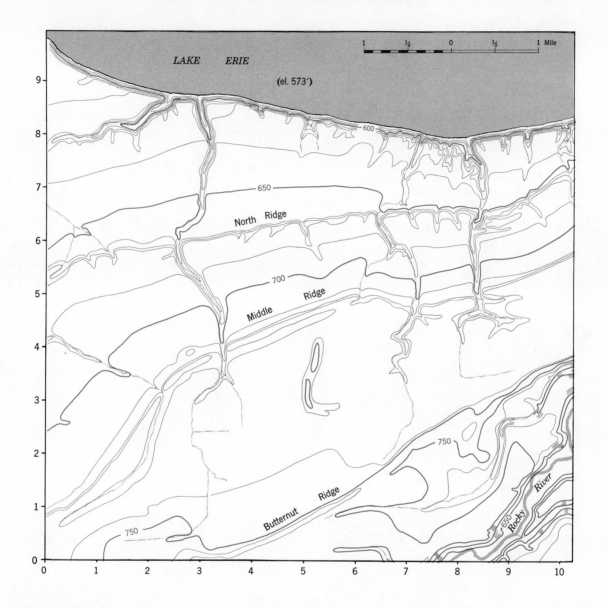

QUESTIONS

Read the explanatory note on page 274.

(a) Construct a profile across the map from north to south, starting at 4.9–9.0. Use the blank graph on page 274. After the profile is completed, paste it into the space provided on page 284.

(Continue on reverse side of page)

(b) On the profile, label the three ridges. Draw horizontal lines across the profile graph to show the lake level at the time each of the three elevated shorelines was formed.

(c) At 5.2–3.5 is a curious curved ridge. Could this be some type of depositional shore feature? Explain. With what lake level is its development associated?

_____

_____

_____

_____

_____

_____

(d) How high is the present wave-cut scarp along the shore of Lake Erie? _____ ft

(e) With color pencil mark the axis of every hanging valley on the Lake Erie scarp.

(Attach completed profile here)

Group Z

LANDFORMS MADE BY WIND

Text References

Strahler, 1969, *Physical Geography, 3rd Edition,* Chapter 31, pp. 549–563.
Strahler, 1970, *Introduction to Physical Geography, 2nd Edition,* Chapter 25, pp. 372–381.

EXPLANATORY NOTES

EXERCISE Z-1: Crescentic (Barchan) Dunes. *(Source: Sieler, Wash., U.S. Geological Survey topographic map; scale 1:24,000)*

The isolated, crescent-shaped hills on this map are barchan dunes. They lie near the easternmost fringe of a large dune field in the vicinity of Moses Lake, Washington. On many of these barchan dunes, a low ridge curves westward from each end of the crescent, reversing the normal curvature of the barchan.

EXERCISE Z-2: Sand Sea of Transverse Dunes. *(Source: Glamis Southeast, Calif., U.S. Geological Survey topographic map; scale 1:24,000)*

Near Yuma, Arizona, in the dry, hot Sonoran Desert, is the largest active sand dune belt of the United States. The portion shown here consists of barren dunes of loose, pale-yellow sand separated by irregular depressions. A series of parallel ridges, seen cutting diagonally across the southwest corner of the map, forms the southwestern border of the dune belt. Over most of the map, the sand is formed into great ridges separated by deep hollows. High steep slip faces dip toward the southeast and east.

EXERCISE Z-3: Coastal Blow-Out Dunes. *(Source: Dune Acres, Ind., U.S. Geological Survey topographic map; scale 1:24,000)*

This map shows a part of the southern coast of Lake Michigan, set aside for public use as the Indiana Dunes State Park. Abundant supplies of beach sand have accumulated here by shore drifting toward the southern end of Lake Michigan. Strong onshore winds, from northerly and northwesterly directions, have produced a series of large coastal blowout dunes.

EXERCISE Z-4: Hairpin Dunes. *(Source: Idaho Falls South, Idaho, U.S. Geological Survey topographic map; scale 1:24,000)*

Long narrow dune ridges on this map trend southwest to northeast. Here and there a ridge is doubled back on itself to produce the characteristic hairpin form of highly elongated parabolic blowout dunes. The ends of several of the hairpin dunes have been built up into prominent dune masses.

Exercise Z-1 CRESCENTIC (BARCHAN) DUNES

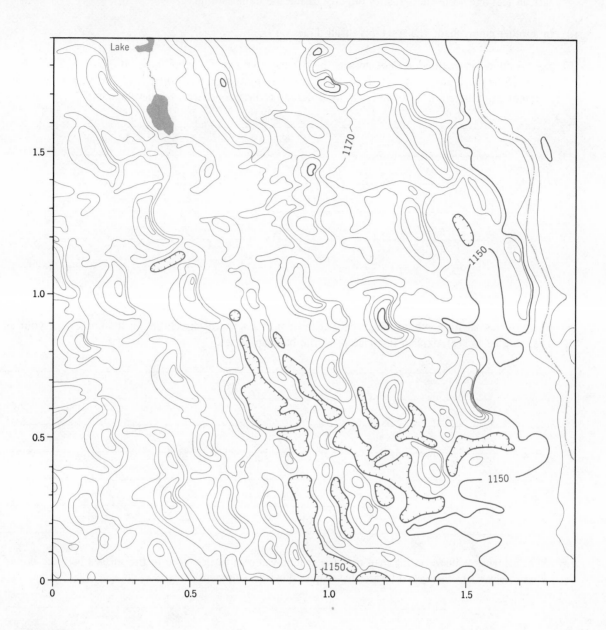

QUESTIONS

Read the explanatory note on page 285.

(a) Give the contour interval and fractional scale of the map.

    C. I. _____ ft   R. F. _____

Z₁ (b) Using color pencil, outline on the map the base of at least twelve well-developed barchan dunes. Indicate the direction of the prevailing wind by a bold arrow.

(c) Choosing the three highest, best-formed dunes, measure the length (transverse to wind) and height of each in feet and write these figures directly beside the dune outline.

(d) In another color, shade the slip-faces of all dunes on the map.

(e) Several dunes on this map do not possess the barchan outline. Examine dunes at 0.6–1.2, 0.1–1.3, 1.1–1.15, and 0.1–0.65. What type of dune is represented by these individuals? Do they indicate a different wind direction? Do they require different surface conditions for development?

_____

_____

_____

_____

_____

_____

(f) Many of the barchans exhibit wing tips that recurve in a westerly direction. In the context of your answer to question (e), explain this feature of the barchan dunes.

_____

_____

_____

_____

_____

_____

(g) What evidence is there on the map that the ground-water table lies close to the surface between dunes? What effect might this ground water have upon dune development?

_____

_____

_____

_____

_____

Exercise Z-2 SAND SEA OF TRANSVERSE DUNES

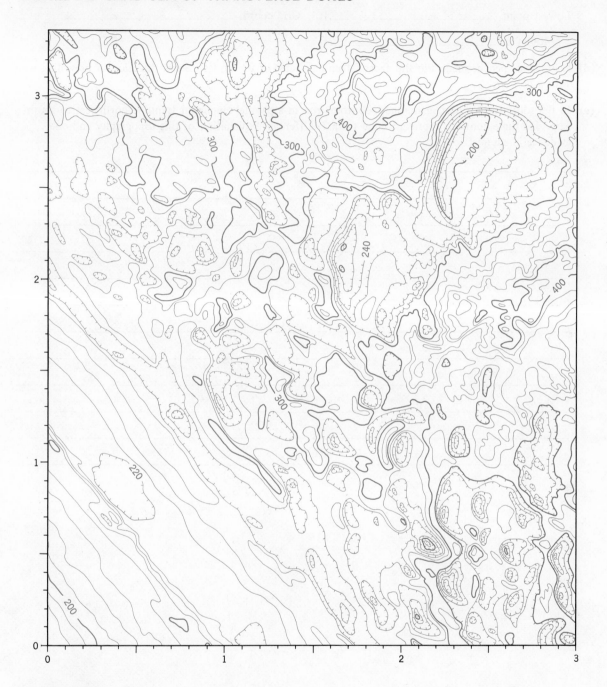

QUESTIONS

Read the explanatory note on page 285.

(a) Give contour and fractional scale for the map above.

    C. I. _____   R. F. _____

(b) Is the map scale larger, or smaller, than the scale of the map in Exercise Z-1?

    _____

Z_2 (c) What is the maximum relief of this dune belt, measuring from the highest dune peak to the deepest point in a dune depression? Give grid coordinates.

Highest peak _____ ft   Grid coord. _____

Lowest point _____ ft   Grid coord. _____

Relief _____ ft

(d) Using color pencil, shade the slip faces (steep lee faces) of the dunes. Show direction of prevailing wind with a bold arrow.

(e) In the southwestern part of the map, contours run in a parallel alignment trending northwest to southeast. Do these contours represent dune forms? Offer an explanation of this topography and cite evidence in support.

_____

_____

_____

_____

_____

_____

_____

_____

_____

_____

_____

_____

Exercise Z-3 COASTAL BLOW—OUT DUNES

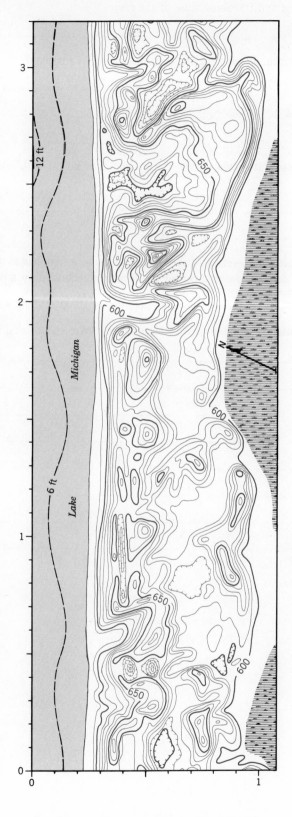

(Answer questions on reverse side of page)

Z₃ Exercise Z-3 QUESTIONS

Read the explanatory note on page 286.

(a) Give the contour interval and fractional scale of the map.

   C. I. _____   R. F. _____

(b) What is the ground distance, in miles, of the long dimension of the map?

   _____ mi

(c) What is the maximum width of the dune belt, in miles?

   _____ mi

(d) Find the highest dune summit shown on the map. Give dune height with respect to a base of 600 ft.
    Give grid coordinates.

   Summit elevation _____ ft   Grid coord. _____

   Dune height _____ ft

(e) Using a color pencil, color each well-developed blow-out dune to emphasize its horseshoe shaped out-
    line. Color only those dunes showing a central depression surrounded by a prominent rim.

(f) Draw a bold arrow on the map to represent the direction of the prevailing wind.

(g) What type and distribution of vegetation would you expect over this coastal dune belt?

   _____

   _____

   _____

   _____

   _____

   _____

   _____

   _____

Exercise Z-4 HAIRPIN DUNES

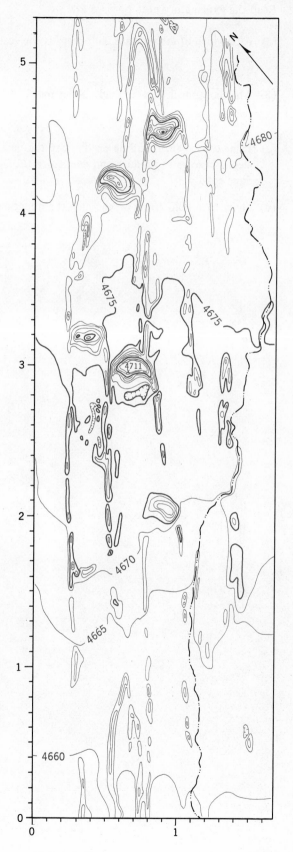

(Answer questions on reverse side of page)

Z₄ Exercise Z-4 QUESTIONS

Read the explanatory note on page 286.

(a) With which of the previous dune maps is the scale of this map most closely matched?

Exercise _____

(b) What contour interval is used on this map?

C. I. _____

(c) Using color pencil, outline on the map the base of all dunes, connecting the individual ridge and hill elements so as to produce and emphasize the outlines of a few simple hairpin dunes. Then color in the dune solidly.

(d) Show by a bold arrow on the map the direction of the prevailing wind.

Group AA

COASTAL PLAINS, HORIZONTAL STRATA, DOMES

Text References

Strahler, 1969, *Physical Geography, 3rd Edition,* Chapter 32, pp. 565–588.
Strahler, 1970, *Introduction to Physical Geography, 2nd Edition,* Chapter 26, pp. 382–398.

EXPLANATORY NOTES

EXERCISE AA-1: Cuestas of the Paris Basin. *(Source: France; scale 1:200,000; Chalons Sheet)*
    This map shows a part of two cuestas of the Paris Basin in the region east of Paris, France. The Argonne cuesta, supporting the Argonne Forest of World War I fame, runs down along the eastern side of the map. It is a deeply dissected, rugged sandstone cuesta with steep scarps on the east side. The Hills of Champagne (Monts de Champagne) comprise a lower but well-defined cuesta running through the western part of the map, with divide summits rising to slightly over 200 meters. Between the two cuestas is a lowland on weak marls and clays, the Wet Champagne (Champagne Humide) in which flows the Aisne River. West from the Hills of Champagne the cuesta backslope descends gradually to form the Dry Champagne (Champagne Pouilleuse), a chalk plain with few surface streams.

EXERCISE AA-2: Mesas, Buttes, and Canyons. *(Source: Marsh Pass, Ariz., U.S. Geological Survey topographic map; scale 1:250,000)*
    Erosion of a resistant sandstone layer underlain by a weak shale formation has produced the steep-sided flat-topped mesas, buttes, and plateaus shown on this map of a semiarid part of northern Arizona.

EXERCISE AA-3: Sinkholes. *(Source: Princeton, Ky., U.S. Geological Survey topographic map; scale 1:62,500)*
    Numerous small sinkholes, some containing lakes (solid black), are represented by the closed hachured contours. This topography indicates a limestone formation beneath the surface.

EXERCISE AA-4: Mountainous Dome with Hogbacks.
    This is a synthetic map, not representing any real area, and should be regarded as an idealized diagram for illustrating landforms typical of a maturely dissected dome.

Group AA PROFILE BLANK GRAPHS

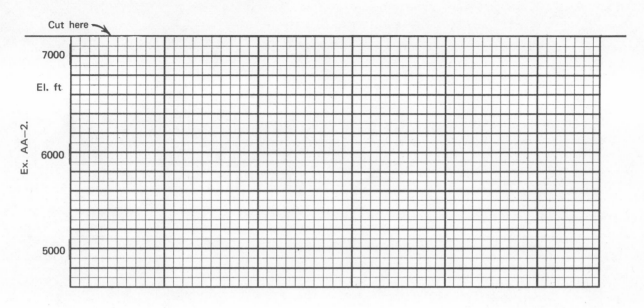

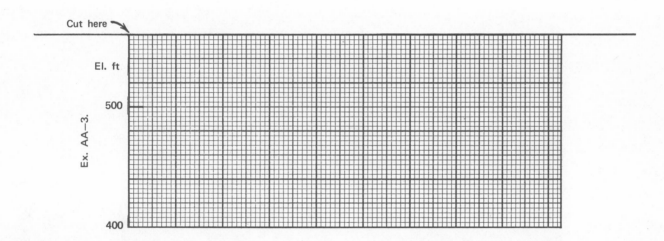

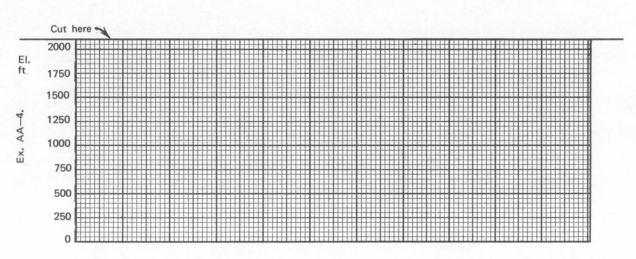

Exercise AA-1 CUESTAS OF THE PARIS BASIN

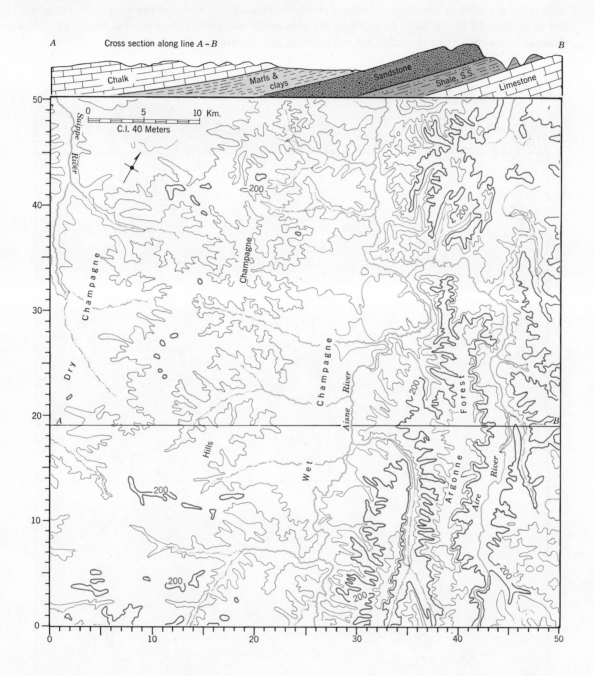

A   Cross section along line A – B   B

Chalk   Marls & clays   Sandstone   Shale, S.S.   Limestone

0   5   10 Km.

C.I. 40 Meters

Suippe River

Champagne

Dry

Champagne

Champagne River

Aisne

Forest

Wet

Hills

Argonne

Aire River

QUESTIONS

Read the explanatory note on page 295.

(a) Give the equivalent value in feet for the contour interval used on this map (40 m).

_____

(b) Determine the width of the map, in miles.

_____

(Continue on reverse side of page)   **299**

(c) On the map on page 299, draw in the complete stream net, including streams indicated only by V-indentations of contours. Use the following color scheme: subsequent streams, blue; resequent streams, red; obsequent streams, green. The result will be a trellis pattern typical of a mature coastal plain.

(d) On the duplicate map below, draw in the geologic boundaries separating the zones underlain by various rock types as shown in the structure section above the map. First, mark off the boundaries along the line of section AB on the map, then extend the lines north and south as best fits the topography. Color chalk and limestone areas blue; clay and marl, green; and sandstone, yellow.

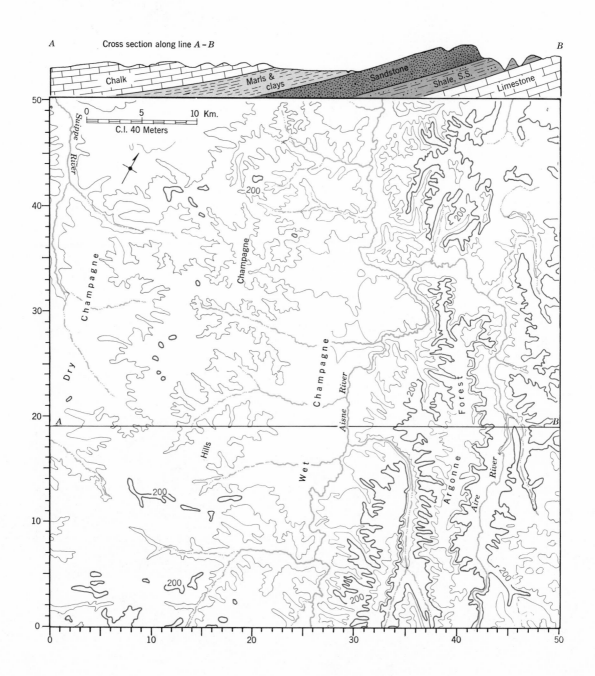

Exercise AA-2 MESAS, BUTTES, AND CANYONS

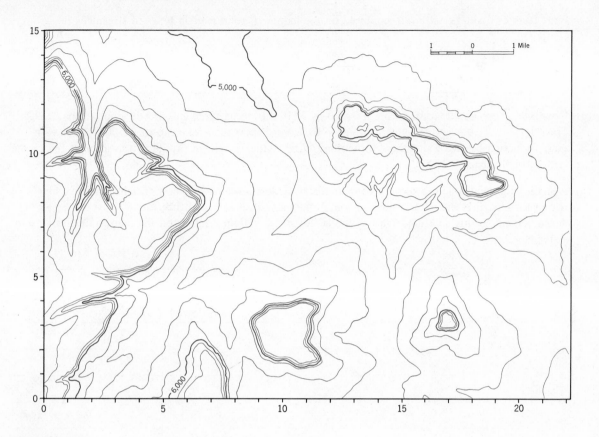

QUESTIONS

Read the explanatory note on page 295.

(a) What contour interval is used on the map above.

C. I. _____

(b) Determine the width of the map area, in miles.

_____ mi

(c) Locate by grid coordinates and give the elevation of the highest point on the map.

Grid coord. _____   Elevation _____ ft

(d) How high is the cliff at 4.5–5.5?

_____ ft

(Continue on reverse side of page)

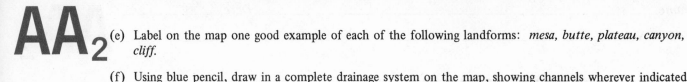

(e) Label on the map one good example of each of the following landforms: *mesa, butte, plateau, canyon, cliff.*

(f) Using blue pencil, draw in a complete drainage system on the map, showing channels wherever indicated by contours.

What form of drainage pattern is exhibited on the map? Of what genetic types of streams is it composed?

_____

_____

(g) Construct a topographic profile from 0.0–3.0 to 22.0–3.0, using the blank profile graph on page 297. Then draw under the profile a line to indicate the contact of a sandstone cap rock 500-ft thick with a shale formation below. Label these formations. Attach the completed profile to the space at the bottom of this page.

(h) Assuming the sandstone cap rock to be of uniform thickness wherever it now remains, have we any reason to think that the layer is not horizontal, but instead, that it is slightly tilted or bent? Cite evidence bearing on this question. Place a number of strike-and-dip symbols on the map to illustrate your statement.

_____

_____

_____

_____

_____

_____

_____

_____

_____

(Attach completed profile here)

Exercise AA-3   SINKHOLES

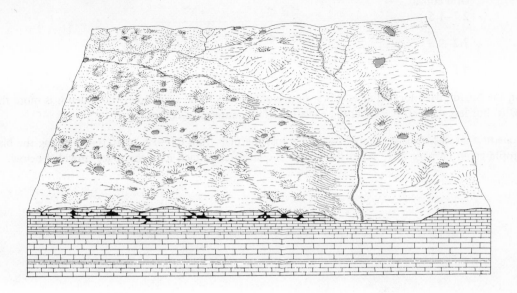

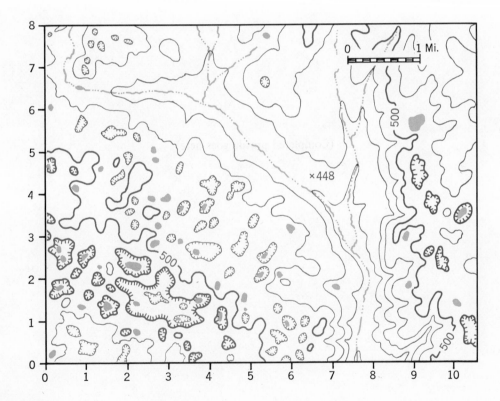

QUESTIONS

Read the explanatory note on page 295.

(a) What contour interval is used on the map above? Refer to the numbered heavy contour line and to the spot height at 6.5–4.4.

C. I. _____

(Continue on opposite side of page)

AA$_3$

(b) Estimate the depth of each of the sinkholes whose location is given below by grid coordinates. By "depth" is meant the difference in elevation between the lowest outlet point on the rim of the depression and the deepest point on the bottom of the depression. Give limiting values, as for example: $40 < d < 80$, meaning "depth greater than 40 ft but less than 80 ft."

Grid coord.

2.7–1.5 _____ $< d <$ _____

2.2–2.3 _____ $< d <$ _____

9.1–4.5 _____ $< d <$ _____

(c) On the broad divide located at 6.5–5.5, draw contours to show a sinkhole whose depth is more than 40 ft, but less than 80 ft. Label the elevation of the outermost contour.

(d) Construct an east-west topographic profile across the map from 0.0–1.6 to 10.6–1.6, using the blank profile graph on page 297. After the profile is completed, attach it to the space provided below.

(Completed profile goes here)

Exercise AA-4 MOUNTAINOUS DOME WITH HOGBACKS

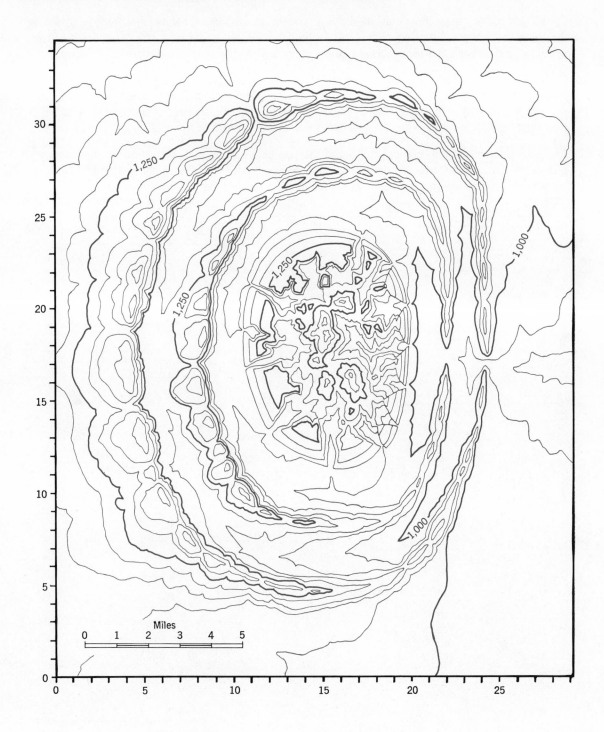

Read the explanatory note on page 295.

(Continue on reverse side of page)

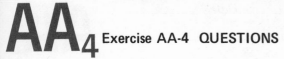

Exercise AA-4 QUESTIONS

(a) Label on the map good examples of the following: *hogback, flatiron, subsequent valley, central crystalline area,* and *watergap.* (Use initials: H, F, SV, CCA, and W.)

(b) Using color pencils, draw in a complete drainage system on the map, showing all streams indicated by the contours. Use the following colors: subsequent streams, blue; resequent streams, red; obsequent streams, green; insequent streams, black. Add a color key in the lower right corner of the map.

(c) Construct a topographic profile from 0–19 to 29–19, using the blank graph on page 297. Then add a geologic structure section consisting of layers of sandstone and shale drawn to conform with the hogbacks, flatirons, and subsequent valleys. Show crystalline rocks in the core of the dome. Attach the completed profile and structure section to the space at the bottom of this page.

(d) Assuming the sandstone formations that make the two hogback ridges to be of uniform thickness where present over this region, why are the hogback ridges broad and cuestalike on the west side? Does your answer explain why the major streams drain out through the east side of the dome?

_____

_____

_____

_____

_____

_____

_____

_____

_____

(Attach completed profile here.)

FOLDS, FAULTS, AND FAULT BLOCKS

Text References

Strahler, 1969, *Physical Geography, 3rd Edition*, Chapter 33, pp. 589–602.
Strahler, 1970, *Introduction to Physical Geography, 2nd Edition*, Chapter 27, pp. 400–407.

EXPLANATORY NOTES

EXERCISE BB-1: Mountains Developed on Folded Strata.

This is a synthetic map, not representing any real topography, and should be regarded as an idealized diagram illustrating the ridge and valley forms typical of a maturely dissected region of folded strata.

The diagram below shows topographic and structural elements of a series of eroded open folds. A sandstone formation and conglomerate formation are ridge-formers; the thick shales above and below are valley-formers.

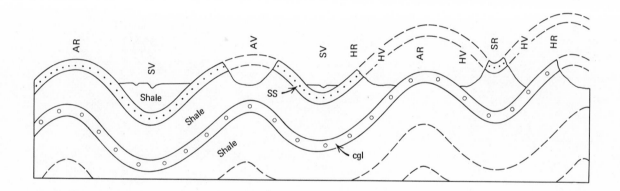

EXERCISE BB-2: Fault Scarps and Graben. *(Source: Klamath, Oregon, U.S. Geological Survey topographic map; scale 1:250,000)*

The steep, simple scarps trending northwest to southeast on this map are fault scarps. Upper Klamath Lake occupies a graben and is bounded by fault scarps on both sides. Swan Lake Valley is a downtilted block with a fault scarp on the east side only.

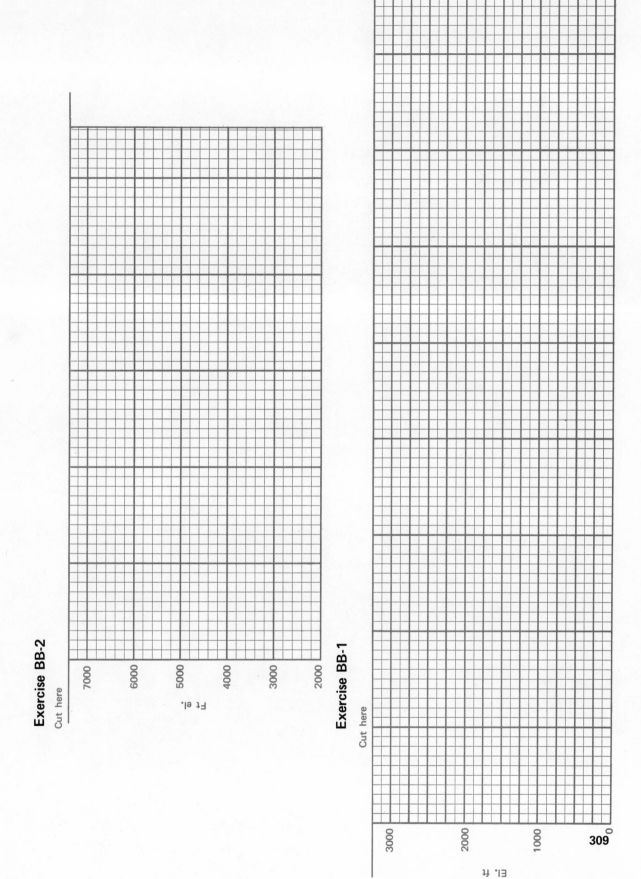

Exercise BB-2

Cut here

7000

6000

5000

4000

3000

2000

Ft el.

Exercise BB-1

Cut here

3000

2000

1000

309 0

El. ft

Exercise BB-1 MOUNTAINS DEVELOPED ON FOLDED STRATA

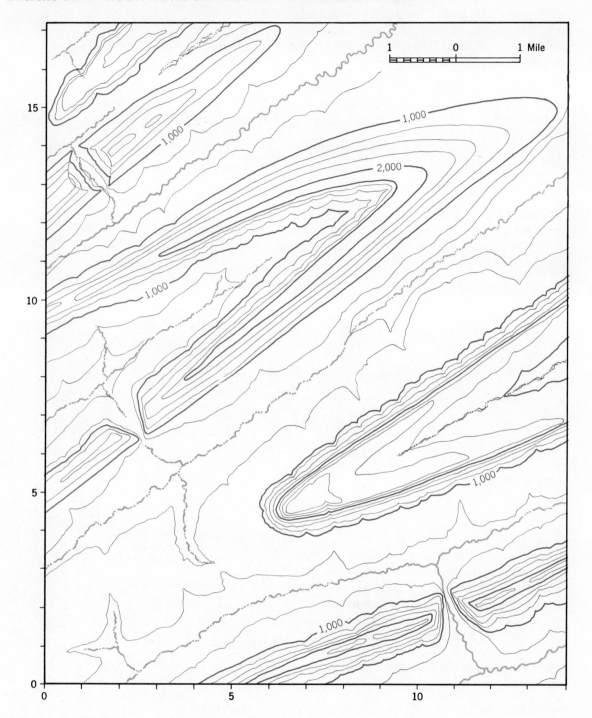

Read the explanatory note on page 307.

(Continue on reverse side of page)

(a) Label on the map each ridge and valley using the initials for each of the following landforms: anticlinal ridge *(AR)*, synclinal ridge *(SR)*, homoclinal ridge *(HR)*, anticlinal valley *(AV)*, synclinal valley *(SV)*, homoclinal valley *(HV)*. Refer to the diagram on page 307 for guidance.

(b) On the map, draw in a complete drainage system using the following colors: subsequent streams, blue; resequent streams, red; obsequent streams, green.

(c) What name is given to the type of drainage pattern shown on this map?

_____

(d) Explain the fact that the deep gap in the ridge at 2.5– 6.5 now contains no through-flowing stream, although it resembles the watergap at 11.0–2.0. What drainage change appears to have occurred here?

_____

_____

_____   (Attach completed profile here.)

_____

_____

_____

_____

_____

_____

(e) Construct a topographic profile from the upper left-hand corner of the map to the lower right-hand corner. Use the blank profile graph on page 309. Draw in a complete geologic structure section consisting of sandstone and shale formations in agreement with your interpretation of landforms in Question (a). Attach the completed profile and structure section to the space at the right on this page.

(f) Enter numerous strike-and-dip symbols on the ridges over the map. Show axes of folds and their direction of plunge by long arrows. Label the arrows "A" or "S" for "anticline" or "syncline."

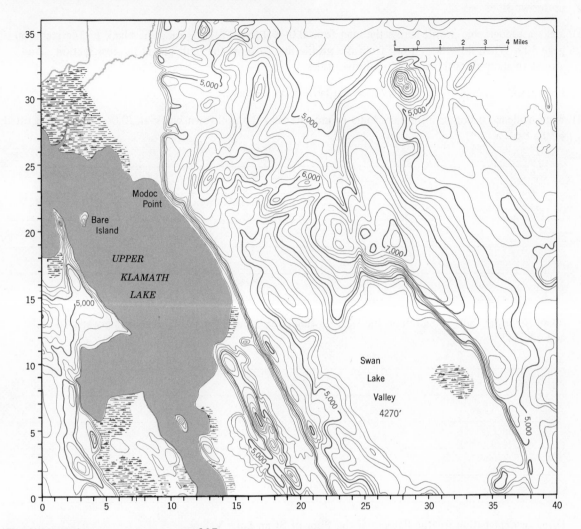

Exercise BB-2 FAULT SCARPS AND GRABEN

Read the explanatory note on page 307.

(Continue with questions on reverse side of page)

(Attach completed profile here.)

(a) In black pencil, draw on the map all fault lines which you can confidently interpret from the topographic forms. Write the letters D and U on opposite sides of each fault to indicate downthrown and upthrown sides.

(b) Make a topographic profile across the map from 0.0–8.0 to 40.0–8.0, using the blank profile graph on page 309. Then draw lines down from the profile line to show the fault planes in cross section. Add arrows to show downthrown and upthrown sides.

(c) Find a good example of a *fault splinter* and label it on the map.

(d) What evidence is present in the contours to indicate that the upthrown block at 20.0–7.0 has been tilted to the east?

_____

_____

_____

_____

_____

_____

(e) What effect has faulting had upon the west-flowing streams reaching the fault scarp between 10–27 and 10–34?

_____

_____

_____

_____

_____

_____

(f) Offer an explanation for the flatness of the floor of Swan Lake Valley.

_____

_____

_____

_____

_____

_____

Group CC

VOLCANIC LANDFORMS

Text References

Strahler, 1969, *Physical Geography, 3rd Edition*, Chapter 34, pp. 603–618.
Strahler, 1970, *Introduction to Physical Geography, 2nd Edition*, Chapter 28, pp. 409–421.

EXPLANATORY NOTES

EXERCISE CC-1: Volcano. *(Source: Dunsmuir, Calif., U.S. Geological Survey topographic map; scale 1:125,000)*

   This map shows Mount Shasta, a great composite volcano of the Cascade Range. The photograph below was taken from the southwest. The main part of the volcano is dissected by streams and glaciers, and no longer shows a crater. Several small glaciers, shown gray on the map, remain on the mountain. Shastina, a subsidiary cone, is seen on the western slope of the main cone. Shastina is relatively young in date of formation and still shows a crater rim.

(Infrared photograph by Eliot Blackwelder.)

Cut here

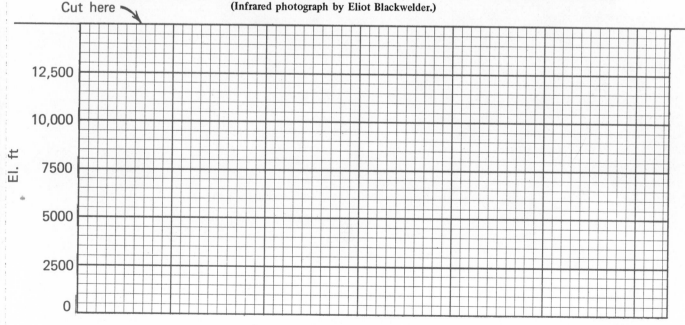

El. ft

EXPLANATORY NOTES *(continued)*

EXERCISE CC-2: Volcanic Neck and Dikes. *(Source: Ship Rock, N.M., U.S. Geological Survey topographic map; scale 1:62,500)*

    Ship Rock, a steep-sided volcanic neck, rises above a broad plain, underlain by soft shales which have been easily removed by running water, leaving the harder volcanic rocks standing in bold relief. The air photograph below shows the map area viewed from the northeast. Details shown on the photograph can easily be found on the map. Two great dikes extend radially outward, southward and westward from the neck.

(Spence Air Photos.)

Exercise CC-1 VOLCANO

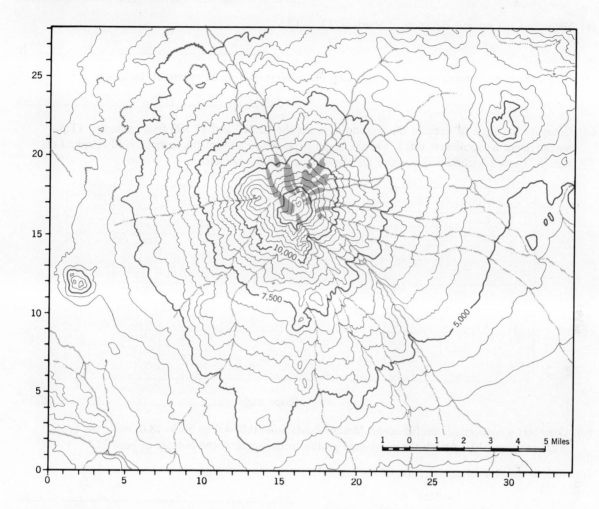

Read the explanatory note on page 315. Study the photograph on page 315 and compare with map details.

(Answer questions on reverse side of page.)

(Attach completed profile here.)

Exercise CC-1 QUESTIONS

(a) What is the summit elevation of Mount Shasta?

_____ ft

(b) Determine the summit elevation of Shastina, 13.5–17.5.

_____ ft

(c) How wide is the volcano at its base, assuming the 5000-ft contour to represent the base?

_____ mi

(d) Compute the angle of slope of the volcano between the 10,000 and 12,500 foot contours. (Take measurement on southwest side.) Use the graph paper below to plot the vertical and horizontal distances. Draw a triangle and measure the slope angle with a protractor.

Slope angle _____ °

(e) Construct a topographic profile across Mount Shasta from 0.0–4.0 to 30.0–28.0, using the profile graph on page 315. Attach the completed profile to the space at the bottom of page 317.

(f) What is the vertical exaggeration of the profile?

_____

(g) The serrate, or sawtooth contours near 9.0–26.0 mean that a rough, blocky lava flow of recent date is present. Give grid coordinates of the source of this lava, as closely as you can locate it from the contour indications.

_____

(h) Locate by grid coordinates two similar lava flows.

_____   _____

(i) What is the origin of the round hill at 2.0–12.0?

_____

_____

Exercise CC-2 VOLCANIC NECK AND DIKES

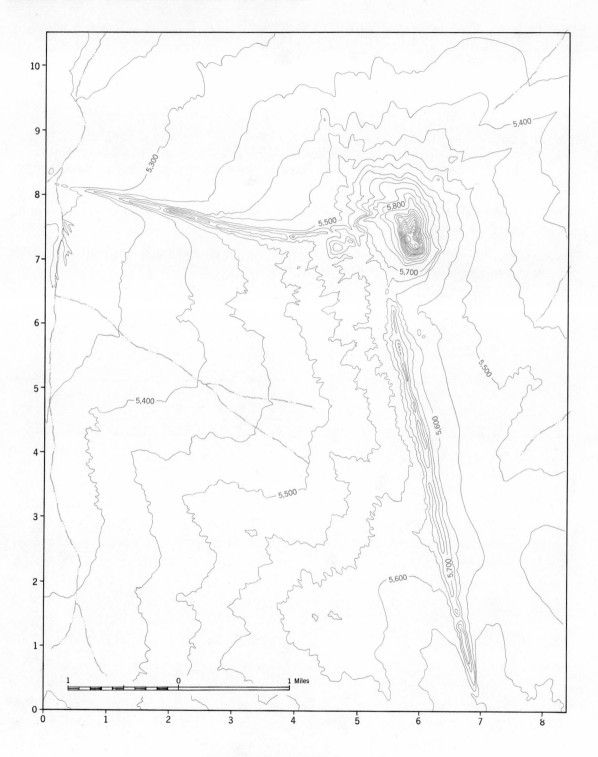

(Questions on reverse side of page)

CC₂

Exercise CC-2 QUESTIONS

(a) Give the contour interval used on the map.

C. I. _____

(b) What is the summit elevation of Ship Rock, 5.8—7.3?

_____ ft

(c) How high is the dike at 6.7—1.2?

_____ ft

(d) In red pencil color on the map all volcanic rock. The dikes should be shown as thin red lines. In addition to the two great dikes, at least two small dikes are indicated by sharply pointed contours. Locate three small pipes of volcanic rock which show on the photograph on page 316. Color these pipes red.

(e) Study the air photograph on page 316 in relation to the map. Draw on the map a line to represent the center line of the photograph.

(f) Contour near 5.0—6.0 are highly crenulate (involuted). What is the significance of this contour form in terms of landforms present? What type of rock is indicated?

_____

_____

_____

_____

_____

_____